3

THE
2016 CHARLTON
COIN GUIDE
55th EDITION

Dealer's buying prices for
Canadian, Newfoundland and Maritime coinage,
Canadian Medals, Tokens and Paper Money,
United States and World Gold Coinage

Editor
W. K. Cross

Publisher
Mark Drake

The Charlton Press

Toronto, Ontario, Canada

Library and Archives Canada Cataloguing this publication as follows

Charlton, J.E., 1911
    Charlton coin guide

18th- ed.; 1978--
Continues: Charlton J. E., 1911- Coin guide of Canadian, Newfoundland and
    Maritime coinage, ISSN 0701-8223.
ISSN 0706-0459
ISBN 978-0-88968-373-0 (55th edition)

        1. Coins, Canadian—Periodicals.   2. Coins, Canadian--Priices--Periodicals
I. Title.

CJ1864.C5114 18- 1978-   737.4'9'71   C79-030323-X

**Printed in Canada
in the Province of Quebec**

The Charlton Press

P. O. Box 414, Station F
Toronto, Ontario. M4Y 2L8 Canada
Tel: 416-962-2665; Toll free: 1-866-663-8827
Fax: 416-964-1632
www.charltonpress.com; E-mail: chpress@charltonpress.com

8

CONTENTS

INDEX OF ADVERTISERS

INTRODUCTION

It is more difficult to obtain old coins in circulation, much more so than it was twenty-five years ago. For the most part silver no longer circulates, since its bullion value now exceeds its face value. Generally speaking, the only pre-1968 coins in circulation are one-cent and five-cent pieces, and these seldom pre-date 1953. Older coins must now be purchased through dealers.

BUYING AND SELLING PRICES

Buying prices are what dealers pay for coins. Selling prices are what dealers charge for coins. Generally, dealers will pay 40% to 60% of their selling price. It should be remembered all dealers will pay according to their needs. They will pay well for what they need immediately, but for those coins for which there is no demand, even if they have a high retail value, they will offer substantially less.

The prices shown in this book represent averages or estimates of buying prices and should serve as a guide in negotiating fair prices when buying or selling. Also a clearer idea of which coins are in demand by collectors and dealers can be developed by studying the guide.

Coins should not be mailed for appraisal unless a written response to an inquiry is received from the dealer. If coins are mailed, then they should be sent by registered mail, insured, accompanied by a list of the coins sent, with a complete return address and return postage.

HANDLING AND CLEANING COINS

Coins should be handled by the edges only. Avoid touching the surfaces. Many collectors have found too late that fingerprints cannot be removed from coins or other metal valuables. Proof and specimen quality coins must be handled with extra care since their high lustre is very fragile.

Inevitably, the question of whether to clean coins or not will arise. Probably the best course to follow is, when in doubt don't, until you have contacted an experienced collector or dealer.

The tarnish on silver coins can be removed, but it will not necessarily raise the value. If the tarnish is very thick, then its removal could leave the coin looking much worse.

Nickel coins seldom require cleaning, and only soap and water are safe since nickel is a fairly active metal. Copper and bronze should not be cleaned by anyone who is not knowledgeable in the chemical properties of these metals and their alloys.

Whatever the metal, abrasives must never be used. There are many polishes on the market which are designed for silverware, copper and brass. These must not be used with coins. The results are disastrous.

HANDLING AND CLEANING PAPER MONEY

Inexperienced collectors should always use great care when handling notes. Notes should be handled as little as possible, since oil and perspiration from one's skin can damage and devalue a note. Care should be taken to ensure that unfolded or uncreased notes remain so, and that even marginal tears or abrasions are avoided. Under no circumstances should one ever wash or otherwise try to clean a note since it is likely that the note's value will be considerably reduced. The same is true for ironing or pressing. It should be avoided.

MINT MARKS

A mint mark is a letter stamped on a coin to designate the mint that produced the coins. Canadian decimal coinage issued prior to 1908 was struck at either the Tower Mint, London, in which case it has no mint mark, or at the Heaton Mint in Birmingham. The Birmingham coins have a small "H" as a mint mark. Since 1908 all Canadian coins have been struck at the Ottawa or Winnipeg Mints, with no mint marks, except the Canadian sovereigns which were identified by a small "C" above the date and a "W" when struck at Winnipeg. Newfoundland's coinage was struck at either London, Birmingham, or Ottawa. The Tower Mint coins had no marks, the Birmingham coins had an "H," and the Ottawa coins had a "C," except for the 1940 and 1942 cent pieces.

The coinage of New Brunswick and Nova Scotia had no mint marks because it was struck at the Tower Mint. Prince Edward Island's coinage was struck at Birmingham, but no mint mark was used because the dies were supplied by the Tower Mint.

COMPOSITION MARKS

Beginning in 1999, the Royal Canadian Mint, after years of development began issuing multiply plated steel coinage. Coins made by this new method carry the letter "P", for plated, on the obverse below the Queen's portrait.

ROYAL CANADIAN MINT LOGO

During mid-2006 the "P" composition mark was replaced by the Royal Canadian Mint logo.

COINS OF CANADA

NOVA SCOTIA

VICTORIA 1861 - 1864

Date and Denomination	Buying Price
1861 half cent	3.00
1864 half cent	3.00
1861 one cent	2.00
1862 one cent	35.00
1864 one cent	2.00

PRINCE EDWARD ISLAND

VICTORIA 1871

Date and Denomination	Buying Price
1871 one cent	2.00

NEW BRUNSWICK

VICTORIA 1861 - 1864

Date and Denomination	Buying Price
1861 half cent	85.00
1861 one cent	3.00
1864 one cent	3.00
1862 five cents	45.00
1864 five cents	45.00
1862 ten cents	45.00
1864 ten cents	50.00
1862 twenty cents	25.00
1864 twenty cents	25.00

IMPORTANT: Buying prices are listed for coins graded VG or better. Bent, damaged or badly worn coins are not collectable and bring a small premium value.

NEWFOUNDLAND

LARGE CENTS

Wide 0   Narrow 0

GEORGE V 1913 - 1936

Date and Mint Mark	Buying Price
1913	.75
1917C	.75
1919C	.75
1920C	.75
1929	.75
1936	.75

VICTORIA 1865 - 1896

Date and Mint Mark	Description	Buying Price
1865		3.00
1872H		2.50
1873		3.00
1876H		3.00
1880	Wide 0	2.50
1880	Narrow 0	125.00
1885		30.00
1888		20.00
1890		2.00
1894		2.00
1896		2.00

SMALL CENTS

GEORGE VI 1938 - 1947

Date and Mint Mark	Description	Buying Price
1938		.25
1940		.25
1940	Re-engraved Date	15.00
1941C		.25
1942		.20
1943C		.20
1944C		.20
1947C		.20

EDWARD VII 1904 - 1909

Date and Mint Mark	Buying Price
1904H	6.00
1907	2.00
1909	2.00

FIVE CENTS

VICTORIA 1865 - 1880

Date and Mint Mark	Buying Price
1865	25.00
1870	75.00
1872H	50.00
1873	100.00
1873H	500.00
1876H	100.00
1880	50.00

VICTORIA 1881 - 1896

Date and Mint Mark	Buying Price
1881	35.00
1882H	25.00
1885	100.00
1888	50.00
1890	7.00
1894	10.00
1896	7.00

EDWARD VII 1903 - 1908

Date and Mint Mark	Buying Price
1903	3.00
1904H	2.00
1908	1.00

GEORGE V 1912 - 1929

Date and Mint Mark	Buying Price
1912	1.00
1917C	1.00
1919C	2.00
1929	1.00

GEORGE VI 1938 - 1947

Date and Mint Mark	Buying Price
1938	.75
1940C	.75
1941C	.75
1942C	.75
1943C	.75
1944C	.75
1945C	.75
1946C	200.00
1947C	1.00

TEN CENTS

VICTORIA 1865 - 1896

Date and Mint Mark	Buying Price
1865	25.00
1870	150.00
1872H	15.00
1873	50.00
1876H	50.00
1880	40.00
1882H	35.00
1885	125.00
1888	35.00
1890	7.00
1894	7.00
1896	7.00

EDWARD VII 1903 - 1904

Date and Mint Mark	Buying Price
1903	3.00
1904H	1.75

GEORGE V 1912 -1919

Date and Mint Mark	Buying Price
1912	1.00
1917C	1.00
1919C	1.00

IMPORTANT: Buying prices are listed for coins graded VG or better. Bent, damaged or badly worn coins are not collectable and bring a small premium value.

GEORGE VI 1938 - 1947

Date and Mint Mark	Buying Price
1938	1.00
1940	1.00
1941C	1.00
1942C	1.00
1943C	1.00
1944C	1.00
1945C	1.00
1946C	1.00
1947C	1.00

TWENTY CENTS

VICTORIA 1865 - 1900

Date and Mint Mark	Buying Price
1865	15.00
1870	15.00
1872H	10.00
1873	20.00
1876H	20.00
1880	25.00
1881	12.00
1882H	10.00
1885	12.00
1888	10.00
1890	8.00
1894	8.00
1896	8.00
1899	5.00
1900	5.00

EDWARD VII 1904

Date and Mint Mark	Buying Price
1904H	10.00

GEORGE V 1912

Date and Mint Mark	Buying Price
1912	2.25

TWENTY-FIVE CENTS

GEORGE V 1917 - 1919

Date and Mint Mark	Buying Price
1917C	2.50
1919C	2.50

IMPORTANT: A mint mark is a letter stamped on a coin to designate the mint that produced the coin. The Canadian Mint used the letter "C" or "W," while the Heaton Mint in England used the letter "H."

IMPORTANT: Buying prices listed are for coins graded VG or better. Bent, damaged or badly worn coins are not collectable and bring a small premium value

FIFTY CENTS

VICTORIA 1870 - 1900

Date and Mint Mark	Buying Price
1870	20.00
1872H	15.00
1873	50.00
1874	25.00
1876H	35.00
1880	35.00
1881	25.00
1882H	15.00
1885	30.00
1888	35.00
1894	10.00
1896	6.00
1898	6.00
1899	5.50
1900	5.50

EDWARD VII 1904 - 1909

Date and Mint Mark	Buying Price
1904H	5.00
1907	5.00
1908	5.00
1909	5.00

GEORGE V 1911 - 1919

Date and Mint Mark	Buying Price
1911	5.00
1917C	5.00
1918C	5.00
1919C	5.00

TWO DOLLARS GOLD

VICTORIA 1865 - 1888

Date and Mint Mark	Buying Price
1865	200.00
1870	200.00
1872	225.00
1880	700.00
1881	175.00
1882H	175.00
1885	175.00
1888	175.00

Note: Two dollar gold coins must be VF condition or better. Damaged, bent or holed coins are bought for gold content.

PROVINCE OF CANADA

LARGE CENTS

Wide 9/8 (W9/8)　　　Narrow 9 (N9)

VICTORIA 1858 - 1859

Date and Mint Mark	Buying Price
1858	40.00
1859 N9	2.00
1859 N9 Brass *	4,000.00
1859 W9/8	20.00

FIVE CENTS

Large date　　　　Small date

VICTORIA 1858

Date and Mint Mark	Buying Price
1858 SD	15.00
1858 LD	100.00

TEN CENTS

VICTORIA 1858

Date and Mint Mark	Buying Price
1858	20.00
1858 8/5	500.00

Note: * Brass metal is yellow in colour.

TWENTY CENTS

VICTORIA 1858

Date and Mint Mark	Buying Price
1858	45.00

CANADA

LARGE CENTS

 Small date Small leaves (SD SL)　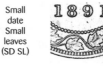 Large date Large leaves (LL LD)

VICTORIA 1876 - 1901

Date and Mint Mark	Buying Price
1876H	2.00
1881H	3.50
1882H	3.50
1884	2.50
1886	4.00
1887	2.50
1888	2.50
1890H	5.00
1891 LL LD	5.00
1891 LL SD	35.00
1891 SL SD	25.00
1892	4.00
1893	2.00
1894	7.50
1895	4.00
1896	2.50
1897	2.50
1898H	5.00
1899	2.50
1900	5.00
1900H	2.00
1901	2.00

1936 Dot

EDWARD VII 1902 - 1910

Date and Mint Mark	Buying Price
1902	1.00
1903	1.00
1904	1.00
1905	1.00
1906	1.00
1907	1.00
1907H	7.00
1908	1.00
1909	1.00
1910	1.00

GEORGE V 1920 - 1936

Date and Mint Mark	Description	Buying Price
1920		.05
1921		.05
1922		10.00
1923		15.00
1924		5.00
1925		15.00
1926		1.25
1927		.05
1928		.05
1929		.05
1930		.05
1931		.05
1932		.05
1933		.05
1934		.05
1935		.05
1936		.05
1936	Dot	100,000.00

Note: The 1936 Dot one cent coin is very rare, only three are confirmed. Examples must be authenticated and certified as counterfiet examples do exist.

GEORGE V 1911 - 1920

Date and Mint Mark	Buying Price
1911	.25
1912	.25
1913	.25
1914	.25
1915	.25
1916	.25
1917	.25
1918	.25
1919	.25
1920	.25

SMALL CENTS

1947 Maple Leaf Blunt 7	1947 Maple Leaf Pointed 7

GEORGE VI 1937 - 1947

Date and Mint Mark	Description	Buying Price
1937 to 1947		.01
1947	Maple Leaf, Blunt 7	.10
1947	Maple Leaf, Pointed 7	.01

Centennial

"A" points to denticles

"A" points between denticles

GEORGE VI 1948 - 1952

Date and Mint Mark	Description	Buying Price
1948	"A" Points to	2.00
1948	"A" Between	.10
1949	"A" Points to	2.00
1949	"A" Between	.01
1950 to 1952		.01

ELIZABETH II, TIARA PORTRAIT, 1965 - 1981

Date and Mint Mark	Description	Buying Price
1965 to 1966		.01
1967	Centennial	.01
1968 to 1981		.01

Blunt 5

Pointed 5

ELIZABETH II, TIARA PORTRAIT, 1982 - 1989

Date and Mint Mark	Description	Buying Price
1982 to 1984		.01
1985	Blunt 5	.01
1985	Pointed 5	1.25
1986 to 1989		.01

No shoulder fold

Shoulder Fold

ELIZABETH II, LAUREATED PORTRAIT, 1953 - 1964

Date and Mint Mark	Description	Buying Price
1953	NSF	.01
1953	SF	.10
1954	SF	.01
1955	NSF	40.00
1955	SF	.01
1956 to 1964		.01

1867 - 1992

ELIZABETH II, DIADEMED PORTRAIT, 1990 - 1996

Date and Mint Mark	Description	Buying Price
1990 to 1991		.01
1867-1992	Double Date	.01
1993 to 1996		.01

Note: You must sort and identify your own coins. Do not expect a dealer to spend hours sorting them for you.

ELIZABETH II, DIADEMED PORTRAIT, COPPER PLATED ZINC, 1997 - 2003

Date and Mint Mark	Description	Buying Price
1997 to 2001		.01
1952-2002	Double Date	.01
2003		.01

Composition Mark

ELIZABETH II, DIADEMED PORTRAIT, COPPER PLATED STEEL, 1999P - 2003P

Date and Mint Mark	Description	Buying Price
1999P		2.50
2000P		2,000.00
2001P		.01
1952-2002P	Double Date	.01
2003P		.01

ELIZABETH II, UNCROWNED PORTRAIT, COPPER PLATED ZINC, 2003 - 2006

Date and Mint Mark	Buying Price
2003	.01
2004	.01
2005	.01
2006	.01

ELIZABETH II, UNCROWNED PORTRAIT, COPPER PLATED STEEL, 2003P - 2006P

Date and Mint Mark	Buying Price
2003P	.01
2004P	.01
2005P	.01
2006P	.01

Royal Canadian Mint Logo

ELIZABETH II, UNCROWNED PORTRAIT, COPPER PLATED ZINC, LOGO, 2006 - 2010

Date and Mint Mark	Buying Price
2006-2007	.01
2009	.01
2010	.01

ELIZABETH II, UNCROWNED PORTRAIT, COPPER PLATED STEEL, LOGO, 2006 - 2012

Date and Mint Mark	Buying Price
2006-2012	.01

Note: 1. The 2000P one cent was issued to vending companies for test purposes.
2. Copper plated steel cents are magnetic, while the copper plated zinc cents are not.
3. May 4th, 2012 was the last day for striking the one cent coin. After 106 years the Royal Canadian Mint ceased issuing pennies.

FIVE CENTS SILVER

1 8 7 4   1 8 7 4

Plain 4   Crosslet 4

Small H (SH)

Large H (LH)

1 8 7 5   1 8 7 5

1875H Small date   1875H Large date
Short top on 5 (SD)   Long top on 5 (LD)

Small 8 (S8)

Large 8 (L8)

1 9 0 0   1 9 0 0

1900 Small Date (SD)   1900 Large Date (LD)

Maple Leaves (ML)

Holly Leaves (HL)

VICTORIA 1870 - 1901

Date and Mint Mark	Buying Price
1870	10.00
1871	10.00
1872H	10.00
1874H Plain 4	20.00
1874H Crosslet 4	15.00
1875H SD	200.00
1875H LD	225.00
1880H	15.00
1881H	10.00
1882H	10.00
1883H	20.00
1884	100.00
1885	10.00
1886	10.00
1887	15.00
1888	7.00
1889	20.00
1890H	7.00
1891	7.00
1892	7.00
1893	7.00
1894	12.00
1896	7.00
1897	7.00
1898	7.00
1899	7.00
1900 LD	15.00
1900 SD	7.00
1901	6.00

Note: Buying prices are for coins in **Very Good (VG)** condition. Damaged, bent or holed coins will be bought for their bullion value.

EDWARD VII 1902 - 1910

Date and Mint Mark	Buying Price
1902	2.00
1902 LH	2.00
1902 SH	7.00
1903H LH	10.00
1903H SH	2.00
1903	2.00
1904	2.00
1905	2.00
1906	2.00
1907	2.00
1908 S8	7.00
1908 L8	25.00
1909 ML	2.00
1909 HL	3.00
1910 ML	10.00
1910 HL	2.00

GEORGE V 1911 - 1921

Date and Mint Mark	Buying Price
1911	1.00
1912	1.00
1913	1.00
1914	1.00
1915	5.00
1916	1.00
1917	1.00
1918	1.00
1919	1.00
1920	1.00
1921	2,500.00

FIVE CENTS NICKEL

Near 6   Far 6

GEORGE V 1922 - 1936

Date and Mint Mark	Description	Buying Price
1922 to 1924		.10
1925		45.00
1926	Near 6	1.00
1926	Far 6	85.00
1927 to 1936		.10

Tombac Beaver   Tombac "V"

1947 Maple Leaf   1947 Dot

GEORGE VI 1937 - 1947

Date and Mint Mark	Description	Buying Price
1937	Dot	.05
1938 to 1941		.05
1942	Nickel	.05
1942	Tombac Beaver	.15
1943	Tombac V	.10
1944	Tombac V *	15,000.00
1944 to 1945	Steel V	.05
1946 to 1947		.05
1947	Maple Leaf	.05
1947	Dot	15.00

Geo. VI Obverse   Beaver

1951 High Relief   1951 Comm.

A in GRATIA points to a rim denticle

A in GRATIA points between rim denticles

GEORGE VI 1948 - 1952

Date and Mint Mark	Description	Buying Price
1948	Without "ET IND:IMP"	.05
1949 to 1951		.05
1951	Commemorative	.05
1951	High Relief	225.00
1952		.05

No Shoulder Fold
On the obverse note the flared ends of "I" and the closed top of the "E"

Shoulder Fold
On the obverse note the straight-sided "I" and the open top the the "E"

Note: * This 1944 five cent coin is made of the alloy Tombac. It is brassy in colour when new, and brown when used. It is not the common steel composition of the 1944 issue.

| Far Maple Leaf | Near Maple Leaf |

ELIZABETH II, LAUREATED PORTRAIT, 1953 - 1962

Date and Mint Mark	Description	Buying Price
1953	NSF, far	.05
1953	NSF, near	150.00
1953	SF, near	.05
1953	SF. far	75.00
1954	NSF	3,500.00
1954SF to 1962		.05

1964 Extra Water Line

ELIZABETH II, LAUREATED PORTRAIT, 1963 - 1964

Date and Mint Mark	Description	Buying Price
1963 to 1964		.05
1964	Extra Water Line	3.25

1965 Attached Jewel Small Beads

1965 Detached Jewel Large Beads

ELIZABETH II, TIARA PORTRAIT, 1965 - 1966

Date and Mint Mark	Description	Buying Price
1965	Small Beads	.05
1965	Large Beads	30.00
1966		.05

ELIZABETH II, TIARA PORTRAIT, 1967 - 1989

Date and Mint Mark	Description	Buying Price
1967	Centennial	.05
1968 to 1989		.05

1867-1992

| 5¢ 1996 Far 6 "6" Far from"D" in Canada | 5¢ 1996 Near 6 "6" Near "D" in Canada |

ELIZABETH II, DIADEMED PORTRAIT, CUPRO NICKEL,1990 - 2001

Date and Mint Mark	Description	Buying Price
1990		.05
1991		.05
1867-1992	Double Date	.05
1993-1995		.05
1996	Far 6	.05
1996	Near 6	.05
1997-2001		.05

Note: The price of nickel collapsed in 2009, removing all premium on the 5-cent nickel coinage.

Composition
Mark

ELIZABETH II, UNCROWNED PORTRAIT, CUPRO NICKEL, 2006

Date and Mint Mark	Buying Price
2006	.05

Double dates 1952 2002P

ELIZABETH II, DIADEMED PORTRAIT, NICKEL PLATED STEEL, 1999P - 2003P

Date and Mint Mark	Description	Buying Price
1999P	Issued For Testing	5.00
2000P		.05
2001P		.05
1952-2002P	Double Date	.05
2003P		.05

Royal
Canadian
Mint Logo

ELIZABETH II, UNCROWNED PORTRAIT, NICKEL PLATED STEEL, LOGO, 2006 - 2015

Date and Mint Mark	Description	Buying Price
2006 to 2015		.05

Victory
1945-2005

ELIZABETH II, UNCROWNED PORTRAIT, NICKEL PLATED STEEL, 2003P - 2006P

Date and Mint Mark	Description	Buying Price
2003P-2005P		.05
2005P	Victory, 1945-2005	.05
2006P		.05

Note: The nickel plated steel coins are magnetic.

TEN CENTS

 1870 Narrow "0" (N0)
Sides of equal thickness

 1870 Wide "0" (W0)
Right side is thicker

 1886
Small 6 (S6)

 1886 Large,
Pointed 6 (P6)

 1886 Large,
Knobbed 6 (L6)

 1892
2 over 1
Large 9 (L9)

 1892
Normal Date
Small 9 (S9)

 1893
Flat-top 3
Medium 9 (F3)

 1893
Round-top 3
Large 9 (R3)

 1899
Small 9s (S9)

 1899
Large 9s (L9)

VICTORIA 1870 -1901

Date and Mint Mark	Buying Price
1870 N0	15.00
1870 W0	25.00
1871	20.00
1871H	25.00
1872H	100.00
1874H	12.00
1875H	250.00

VICTORIA 1870 - 1901 (cont.)

Date and Mint Mark	Buying Price
1880H	20.00
1881H	20.00
1882H	20.00
1883H	50.00
1884	200.00
1885	50.00
1886 S6	30.00
1886 Pt6	85.00
1886 L6	50.00
1887	45.00
1888	12.00
1889	700.00
1890H	20.00
1891	20.00
1892 L9	250.00
1892 S9	15.00
1893 F3	35.00
1893 R3	700.00
1894	30.00
1896	10.00
1898	10.00
1899 S9	10.00
1899 L9	25.00
1900	10.00
1901	7.00

EDWARD VII 1902 - 1910

Date and Mint Mark	Buying Price
1902	3.00
1902H	3.00
1903	5.00
1903H	3.00
1904	5.00
1905	3.00
1906	3.00
1907	3.00
1908	5.00
1909 VL	3.00
1909 BL	5.00
1910	3.00

Note: Buying prices are for coins in **Very Good (VG)** condition. Coins of lower grades will be bought at lower prices.

Small Leaves   Broad leaves   1969 Small Date   1969 Large Date

GEORGE V 1911 - 1936

1980 Wide 0   1980 Narrow 0

Date and Mint Mark	Description	Buying Price
1911		3.00
1912		.90
1913	Small Leaves	.90
1913	Broad Leaves	50.00
1914 to 1936		.90

ELIZABETH II, TIARA PORTRAIT, 1965 - 1989

Date and Mint Mark	Description	Buying Price
1965 to 1966		.90
1967	Centennial	.60
1968	.500 Fine Silver	.50
1968	Nickel	.10
1969	Large Date	8,000.00
1969	Small Date	.10
1970 to 1979		.10
1980	Wide 0	3.00
1980	Narrow 0	.10
1981 to 1989		.10

GEORGE VI 1937 - 1947

Date and Mint Mark	Description	Buying Price
1937 to 1947		.90
1947	Maple Leaf	.90

GEORGE VI 1948 - 1952

Date and Mint Mark	Description	Buying Price
1948	Without "ET IND"IMP"	1.50
1949 to 1952		.90

1867-1992

ELIZABETH II, DIADEMED PORTRAIT, 1990 - 2000

Date and Mint Mark	Description	Buying Price
1990 to 1991		.10
1992	Double Date	.10
1993 to 2000		.10

ELIZABETH II, LAUREATED PORTRAIT, 1953 - 1964

Date and Mint Mark	Buying Price
1953 to 1964	.90

Composition
Mark

Royal
Canadian
Mint Logo

Year of the Volunteer

ELIZABETH II, UNCROWNED PORTRAIT,
NICKEL PLATED STEEL, LOGO, 2006 - 2015

Date and Mint Mark	Buying Price
2006	.10
2007	.10
2008	.10
2009	.10
2010	.10
2012	.10
2013	.10
2014	.10
2015	.10

Double dates 1952 2002P

ELIZABETH II, DIADEMED PORTRAIT ,
NICKEL PLATED STEEL, 1999P - 2003P

Date and Mint Mark	Description	Buying Price
1999P		2.50
2000P		500.00
2001P	Volunteers	.10
2001P	Bluenose	.10
1952-2002P	Double Date	.10
2003P		.10

ELIZABETH II, UNCROWNED PORTRAIT,
NICKEL PLATED STEEL, 2003P - 2006P

Date and Mint Mark	Buying Price
2003P	.10
2004P	.10
2005P	.10
2006P	.10

TWENTY-FIVE CENTS

Narrow 0 (N0)   Wide 0 (W0)

Small crown (SC)   Large crown (LC)

6 over 7 (6/7)   6 over 6 (6/6)

VICTORIA 1870 - 1901

Date and Mint Mark	Buying Price
1870	15.00
1871	25.00
1871H	25.00
1872H	12.00
1874H	12.00
1875H	350.00
1880H N0	50.00
1880H W0	150.00
1881H	25.00
1882H	25.00
1883H	15.00
1885	150.00
1886	40.00
1886 6/7	85.00
1886 6/6	85.00
1887	125.00
1888	30.00
1889	135.00
1890H	30.00
1891	75.00
1892	15.00
1893	125.00
1894	25.00
1899	10.00
1900	10.00
1901	10.00

EDWARD VII 1902 - 1910

Date and Mint Mark	Buying Price
1902	7.00
1902H	7.00
1903	12.00
1904	20.00
1905	12.00
1906 SC	1,000.00
1906 LC	5.00
1907	5.00
1908	15.00
1909	5.00
1910	5.00

GEORGE V 1911 - 1936

Date and Mint Mark	Description	Buying Price
1911		5.00
1912 to 1914		2.50
1915		15.00
1916 to 1920		2.50
1921		10.00
1927		20.00
1928 to 1936		2.00
1936	Dot	25.00

Note: Buying prices are for coins in **Very Good (VG)** condition. Coins with excessive wear, holed or bent will be discounted from the listed price.

1947 Dot   1947 Maple Leaf

GEORGE VI 1937 - 1947

Date and Mint Mark	Description	Buying Price
1937 to 1947		2.00
1947	Maple Leaf	2.00
1947	Dot	25.00

Centennial   RCMP

1973 Small Bust   1973 Large Bust
120 Obverse Beads   132 Obverse Beads
Far from Rim   Near Rim

GEORGE VI 1948 - 1952

Date and Mint Mark	Descripton	Buying Price
1948	Without "ET IND:IMP"	2.00
1949 to 1952		2.00

ELIZABETH II, TIARA PORTRAIT, 1965 - 1973

Date and Mint Mark	Description	Buying Price
1965 to 1966		2.00
1967	Centennial	1.50
1968	.500 Fine Silver	1.25
1968 to 1972	Nickel	.25
1973	Small Bust	.25
1973	Large Bust	75.00

ELIZABETH II, LAUREATED PORTRAIT, 1953 - 1964

Date and Mint Mark	Description	Buying Price
1953	Large Date	2.00
1953	Small Date	2.00
1954 to 1964		2.00

ELIZABETH II, TIARA PORTRAIT, 1974 - 1989

Date and Mint Mark	Buying Price
1974 to 1989	.25

Note: Victoria, Edward and George V quarters must be **Very Good (VG)** or better.

ELIZABETH II, DIADEMED PORTRAIT, 1990 - 1991

Date	Buying Price
1990	.25
1991	1.00

Prince Edward Island

Ontario

CANADA 125 ANNIVERSARY

Nova Scotia

Quebec

Common Obverse

Saskatchewan

British Columbia

New Brunswick

Northwest Territories

ELIZABETH II, DIADEMED PORTRAIT, 1992

Date and Mint Mark	Description	Buying Price
1992	New Brunswick	.25
1992	Northwest Territories	.25
1992	Newfoundland	.25
1992	Manitoba	.25
1992	Yukon	.25
1992	Alberta	.25
1992	Prince Edward Island	.25
1992	Ontario	.25
1992	Nova Scotia	.25
1992	Quebec	.25
1992	Saskatchewan	.25
1992	British Columbia	.25

Newfoundland

Manitoba

Yukon

Alberta

ELIZABETH II, DIADEMED PORTRAIT, 1992 - 2001

Datae	Buying Price
1992 to 1996	.25
2001	.25

Note: No circulation twenty-five cent coins were issued between 1997 and 2000.

1999 MILLENNIUM QUARTERS

November   December

Common Obverse

ELIZABETH II, DIADEMED PORTRAIT, 1999

Date	Description	Buying Price
1999	January	.25
1999	February	.25
1999	March	.25
1999	April	.25
1999	May	.25
1999	June	.25
1999	July	.25
1999	August	.25
1999	September	.25
1999	October	.25
1999	November	.25
1999	December	.25

January   February

March   April

May   June

July   August

September   October

2000 MILLENNIUM QUARTERS

Common Obverse

January   February

March   April

May | June

July | August

September | October

November | December

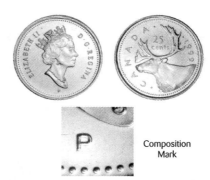

Composition Mark

ELIZABETH II, DIADEMED PORTRAIT, NICKEL PLATED STEEL, 1999P - 2001P

Date and Mint Mark	Buying Price
1999P	5.00
2000P	10,000.00
2001P	.25

ELIZABETH II, DIADEMED PORTRAIT, NICKEL PLATED STEEL, 2002P - 2003P

Date and Mint Mark	Description	Buying Price
1952-2002P	Canada Day, Double Date	.25
1952-2002P	Caribou, Double Date	.25
2003P		.25

ELIZABETH II, DIADEMED PORTRAIT, 2000

Date and Mint Mark	Description	Buying Price
2000	January, Pride	.25
2000	February, Ingenuity	.25
2000	March, Achievement	.25
2000	April, Health	.25
2000	May, Natural Legacy	.25
2000	June, Harmony	.25
2000	July, Celebration	.25
2000	August, Family	.25
2000	September, Wisdom	.25
2000	October. Creativity	.25
2000	November, Freedom	.25
2000	December, Community	.25

First Settlement 2004 | Poppy 2004 and 2008

Note: If a date is not listed then it was not issued for circulation.

Alberta
2005

Saskatchewan
2005

Year of the Veteran
2006

Breast Cancer
2006

ELIZABETH II, UNCROWNED PORTRAIT, NICKEL PLATED STEEL, 2003P - 2006P

Date and Mint Mark	Description	Buying Price
2003P	Caribou	.25
2004P	Caribou	.25
2004P	First Settlement	.25
2004P	Poppy	.25
2005P	Caribou	.25
2005P	Alberta	.25
2005P	Saskatchewan	.25
2005P	Year of the Veteran	.25
2006P	Caribou	.25
2006P	Breast Cancer	.25

Medal of Bravery

Royal
Canadian
Mint Logo

ELIZABETH II, UNCROWNED PORTRAIT, LOGO, NICKEL PLATED STEEL, 2006 - 2008

Date	Description	Buying Price
2006	Caribou	.25
2006	Medal of Bravery	.25
2007	Caribou	.25
2008	Caribou	.25
2008	Poppy	.25

VANCOUVER 2010 PARALYMPIC WINTER GAMES

2007 Obv.
Paralympic Games

Wheelchair Curling

2009 Obv.
Paralympic Games

Ice Sledge Hockey

2007 Vancouver Logo

Wheelchair Curling
Mule

ELIZABETH II, UNCROWNED PORTRAIT, NICKEL PLATED STEEL, 2007 - 2009

Date	Description	Buying Price
2007	Wheelchair Curling	.25
2009	Ice Sledge Hockey	.25
2007	Wheelchair Mule	50.00

Note: The Wheelchair Curling Mule is found only in the uncirculated sets of 2007.

VANCOUVER 2010 WINTER OLYMPIC GAMES

Olympic Obv.

Curling

Ice Hockey

Biathlon

Alpine Skiing

Snowboarding

Freestyle Skiing

Figure Skating

Bobsleigh

Speed Skating

Cross Country Skiing

VANCOUVER 2010 WINTER OLYMPIC GAMES GOLDEN MOMENTS

Men's Ice Hockey
'Standard'

Men's Ice Hockey
'Colourised'

Raised 2

Incused 2

Reverse date 2002

Women's Ice Hockey
'Standard'

Women's Ice Hockey
'Colourised'

Cindy Klassen
'Standard'

Cindy Klassen
'Colourised

ELIZABETH II, UNCROWNED PORTRAIT, NICKEL PLATED STEEL, 2007 - 2009

Date	Description	Buying Price
2007	Curling	.25
2007	Ice Hockey	.25
2007	Biathlon	.25
2007	Alpine Skiing	.25
2008	Snowboarding	.25
2008	Freestyle Skiing	.25
2008	Figure Skating	.25
2008	Bobsleigh	.25
2009	Speed Skating	.25
2009	Cross Country Skiing	.25

ELIZABETH II, UNCROWNED PORTRAIT, NICKEL PLATED STEEL, 2009

Datae	Description	Buying Price
2009	Men's Hockey, Raised 2	.25
2009	Men's Hockey, Colourised, Raised 2	25
2009	Men's Hockey, Colourised, Incused 2	.25
2009	Women's Hockey	.25
2009	Women's Hockey, Colourised	.25
2009	Cindy Klassen	.25
2009	Cindy Klassen, Colourised	.25

2010 Remembrance Day

ELIZABETH II, UNCROWNED PORTRAIT, NICKEL PLATED STEEL, 2009-2015

Date	Description	Buying Price
2009	Caribou	.25
2010	Caribou	.25
2010	Remembrance Day	.25
2011	Caribou	.25
2012	Caribou	.25
2013	Caribou	.25
2014	Caribou	.25
2015	Caribou	.25

LEGENDARY NATURE SERIES

Wood Bison   Wood Bison Colourised

Orca Whale   Orca Whale, Colourised

Peregrine Falcon   Peregrine Falcon Colourised

ELIZABETH II, UNCROWNED PORTRAIT, NICKEL PLATED STEEL, 2011

Date	Description	Buying Price
2011	Wood Bison	.25
2011	Wood Bison, Colourised	.25
2011	Orca Whale	.25
2011	Orca Whale, Colourised	.25
2011	Peregrine Falcon	.25
2011	Peregrine Falcon, Colourised	.25

WAR OF 1812 SERIES

Tecumseh   Tecumseh Colourised

Sir Isaac Brock   Sir Isaac Brock Colourised

Charles-Michel de Salaberry   Charles Michel de Salaberry Colourised

Laura Secord   Laura Secord Colourised

War of 1812 Series (cont.)

ELIZABETH II, UNCROWNED PORTRAIT, NICKEL PLATED STEEL, 2012-2013

Date	Description	Buying Price
2012	Tecumseh	.25
2012	Tecumseh, Colourised	.25
2012	Sir Isaac Brock	.25
2012	Sir Isaac Brock, Colourised	.25
2013	Charles-Michel de Salaberry	.25
2013	Charles-Michel de Salaberry, Colourised	.25
2013	Laura Secord	.25
2013	Laura Secord, Colourised	.25

CANADIAN FLAG

ELIZABETH II, UNCROWNED PORTRAIT, NICKEL PLATED STEEL, 2015

Date	Description	Buying Price
2015	Canadian Flag	.25
2015	Canadian Flag, Colourised	.25

FIFTY CENTS

No LCW   LCW

VICTORIA 1870 - 1901

Date and Mint Mark	Buying Price
1870 No LCW	750.00
1870 LCW	40.00
1871	60.00
1871H	85.00
1872H	40.00
1881H	50.00
1888	250.00
1890H	1,000.00
1892	60.00
1894	300.00
1898	75.00
1899	150.00
1900	45.00
1901	60.00

GEORGE V 1911 - 1936

Date and Mint Mark	Description	Buying Price
1911		12.00
1912		5.50
1913		8.00
1914		20.00
1916		5.50
1917		5.50
1918		5.50
1919		5.50
1920	Wide 0	25.00
1920	Narrow 0	5.00
1921		20,000.00
1929		5.00
1931		20.00
1932		100.00
1934		20.00
1936		25.00

EDWARD VII 1902 - 1910

Date and Mint Mark	Buying Price
1902	15.00
1903H	25.00
1904	150.00
1905	150.00
1906	12.00
1907	12.00
1908	30.00
1909	20.00
1910 VL	15.00
1910 EL	15.00

Straight "7"   Curved "7"
No Maple Leaf   No Maple Leaf

Straight "7"   Curved "7"
With Maple Leaf   With Maple Leaf

Note: Coins must grade **Very Good** or better. Badly worn coins (good) will be priced lower.

36

GEORGE VI 1937 - 1947

Date and Mint Mark	Description	Buying Price
1937 to 1946		4.50
1947	Straight "7"	4.50
1947	Curved "7"	4.50
1947	M.L., Straight "7"	12.00
1947	M.L., Curved "7"	875.00

ELIZABETH II, LAUREATED PORTRAIT, 1953 - 1964

Date and Mint Mark	Description	Buying Price
1953	NSF, SD	4.50
1953	NSF, LD	4.50
1953	SF, LD	4.50
1954 to 1964		4.50

GEORGE VI 1948 - 1952

Date and Mint Mark	Description	Buying Price
1948	Without "ET IND:IMP"	45.00
1949 to 1952		4.50

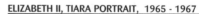

ELIZABETH II, TIARA PORTRAIT, 1965 - 1967

Date and Mint Mark	Description	Buying Price
1965 to 1966		4.50
1967	Centennial	4.50

No shoulder fold   Shoulder fold

1978 Square Jewels

Small date   Large date

1978 Round Jewels

1982 - 118 Large Beads

1982 - 120 Small beads

Composition Mark

ELIZABETH II, DIADEMED PORTRAIT, NICKEL PLATED STEEL, 1999P - 2003P

Date and Mint Mark	Buying Price
1999P	5.00
2000P	3,000.00
2001P	.50
2002P (1952-)	.50
2003P	.50

ELIZABETH II, TIARA PORTRAIT, 1968 - 1989

Date and Mint Mark	Description	Buying Price
1968 to 1977		.50
1978	Square Jewels	.50
1978	Round Jewels	1.00
1979 to 1981		.50
1982	Large Beads	.50
1982	Small Beads	5.00
1983 to 1989		.50

ELIZABETH II, IMPERIAL STATE CROWN PORTRAIT, NICKEL PLATED STEEL, 2002P

Date and Mint Mark	Description	Buying Price
1952-2002P	Jubilee Portrait	.50

ELIZABETH II, DIADEMED PORTRAIT, 1990 - 2000

Date and Mint Mark	Description	Buying Price
1990 to 1991		.50
1867-1992	Double Date	.50
1993 to 1996		.50
1997 to 2000	Modified Reverse	.50

Note: Fifty cents 2002P to 2013 are issued only in rolls of 25, by the Mint.

ELIZABETH II, UNCROWNED PORTRAIT, NICKEL PLATED STEEL, 2004P - 2006P, and 2006 - 2015

Date and Mint Mark	Buying Price
2004P to 2006P	.50
2006 to 2015	.50

SILVER DOLLARS

1935 Obverse

1936 Obverse

1937 to 1947 Obverse

1935 Reverse

1939 Parliament

1949 Newfoundland

Blunt 7

Pointed 7

1952 Water Lines

1952 No Water Lines

1947 Maple Leaf

1947 Dot

GEORGE V 1935 - 1936

Date and Mint Mark	Description	Buying VF Price
1935	Silver Jubilee	18.00
1936	Voyageur	16.00

GEORGE VI 1937 - 1946

Date and Mint Mark	Description	Buying VF Price
1937	Voyageur	13.00
1938	Voyageur	30.00
1939	Royal Visit	10.00 ✓
1945	Voyageur	100.00
1946	Voyageur	20.00

GEORGE VI 1947 - 1952

Date and Mint Mark	Description	Buying VF Price
1947	Blunt 7	60.00
1947	Pointed 7	80.00
1947 Dot	Pointed 7	90.00
1947	Maple Leaf	125.00
1948 ✴	Dei Gratia	700.00 ✓
1949	Newfoundland	11.00 ✓
1950	Voyageur	10.00
1950	Arnprior	10.00
1951	Voyageur	10.00
1951	Arnprior	20.00
1952	Water Lines	10.00
1952	Arnprior	20.00
1952	No Water Lines	10.00

IMPORTANT: The silver dollar buying prices are for problem free coins in **Very Fine (VF)** condition. Damaged coins will bring lower prices.

1953 Obverse

1959 Reverse

1964 Charlottetown

1958 British Columbia

1965 Reverse

1967 Centennial

1955 4 Water Lines

1955 1½ Water Lines

1957 4 Water Lines

1957 1½ Water Lines

ELIZABETH II, LAUREATED PORTRAIT, 1953 - 1960

Date and Mint Mark	Description	Buying EF Price
1953	Voyageur	10.00
1954	Voyageur	10.00
1955	Voyageur	10.00
1955 Arnprior	1½ Waterlines	10.00
1956	Voyageur	11.00
1957	Voyageur	10.00
1957	1½ Waterlines	10.00
1958	British Columbia	10.00
1959	Voyageur	10.00
1960	Voyageur	10.00

ELIZABETH II, TIARA PORTRAIT, 1961 - 1967

Date and Mint Mark	Description	Buying EF Price
1961	Voyageur	10.00
1962	Voyageur	10.00
1963	Voyageur	10.00
1964	Charlottetown	10.00
1965	Voyageur, Medal	10.00
1965	Voyageur, Coinage	1,000.00
1966	Voyageur	10.00
1966 Sm Beads	Voyageur	1,500.00
1967	Centennial, Medal	10.00
1967	Centennial, Coinage	1,000.00

DIE AXIS

The obverse design is considered the primary side of the coin. The die axis is the relationship of the reverse design to the obverse. Consider the obverse die, usually the anvil die in a press, stationary and when installed is the point of reference. The reverse die (moving hammer die) may be turned or set at any of 360 degrees in relation to the set obverse die. If the obverse die is identified by an up-right arrow (↑) then the reverse die may be represented by a second arrow(↑). These arrows form a relationship. Illustrated below are two common die alignments:

Coinage Axis: ↑↓
  Obverse die: ↑
  Reverse die is set 180 degrees opposite: ↓

Medal Axis: ↑↑
  Obverse die: ↑
  Reverse die is set in the matching direction: ↑

NICKEL DOLLARS

Common Obverse

Voyageur Reverse

1968 Island

1968 No Island

Manitoba

British Columbia

Prince Edward Island

Winnipeg

Constitution

Jacques Cartier

ELIZABETH II, TIARA PORTRAIT, 1968 - 1973

Date and Mint Mark	Description	Buying Price
1968	Voyageur	1.00
1968	Small Island	4.00
1968	No Island	2.00
1969	Voyageur	1.00
1970	Manitoba	1.00
1971	British Columbia	1.00
1972	Voyageur	1.00
1973	P.E.I.	1.00

ELIZABETH II, TIARA PORTRAIT, 1974 - 1986

Date and Mint Mark	Description	Buying Price
1974	Winnipeg	1.00
1975 to 1981	Voyageur	1.00
1982	Constitution, Medal	1.00
1982	Consitution, Coinage	500.00
1983	Voyageur	1.00
1984	Jacques Cartier	1.00
1985	Voyageur	1.00
1986	Voyageur	1.00

NICKEL BRONZE DOLLARS

ELIZABETH II, TIARA PORTRAIT, 1987 - 1989

Date and Mint Mark	Description	Buying Price
1987	Loon	1.00
1988	Loon	1.00
1989	Loon	1.00

ELIZABETH II, DIADEMED PORTRAIT, 1992 - 1993

Date and Mint Mark	Description	Buying Price
1867-1992	Double Date	1.00
1993	Loon	1.00

ELIZABETH II, DIADEMED PORTRAIT, 1990 - 1991

Date and Mint Mark	Description	Buying Price
1990 to 1991	Loon	1.00

ELIZABETH II, DIADEMED PORTRAIT, 1994

Date and Mint Mark	Description	Buying Price
1994	Remembrance	1.00
1994	Loon	1.00

CANADA 125 ANNIVERSARY

ELIZABETH II, DIADEMED PORTRAIT, 1995

Date and Mint Mark	Description	Buying Price
1995	Peacekeeping	1.00

ELIZABETH II, DIADEMED PORTRAIT, 1992

Date and Mint Mark	Description	Buying Price
1992	Fireworks on the "Hill"	1.00

IMPORTANT: Do not clean your coins. Coins should be handled carefully. Only experts should consider cleaning. If you are not an expert, the results can be disastrous.

Note: Proof issues of 1987, 1992, 1994 and 1995 were issued by the Numismatic Department of the Royal Canadian Mint.

ELIZABETH II, DIADEMED PORTRAIT, 1995 - 2001

Date and Mint Mark	Description	Buying Price
1995	Loon	1.00
1996	Loon	1.00
1997 to 2001	Not Issued	

ELIZABETH II, DIADEMED PORTRAIT, 2002 - 2003

Date and Mint Mark	Description	Buying Price
1952-2002	Jubilee	1.00
2003	Loon	1.00

2004 Lucky Loonie

2005 Terry Fox

2006 Loon Settling

ELIZABETH II, UNCROWNED PORTRAIT, 2003 - 2006

Date and Mint Mark	Description	Buying Price
2003	Loon	1.00
2004	Loon	1.00
2004	Loon and Olympic Flames	1.00
2005	Loon	1.00
2005	Terry Fox	1.00
2006	Loon	1.00
2006	Loon Settling	1.00

Obv.

2008 Loon Dance

2009 Montreal Canadiens

Vanvcouver Olympic Games

2010 100th Anniv. Navy

2010 Sask. Roughriders

ELIZABETH II, UNCROWNED PORTRAIT, LOGO, 2006 - 2011

Date and Mint Mark	Description	Buying Price
2006	Loon	1.00
2007	Loon	1.00
2008	Loon	1.00
2008	Loon Dance	1.00
2009	Loon	1.00
2009	Montreal Canadiens	1.00
2010	Loon	1.00
2010	Vancouver 2010 Olympics	1.00
2010	100th Anniv. Navy	1.00
2010	Saskatchewan Roughriders	1.00
2011	Loon	1.00

2011 Parks Canada

Obv.

2012-2015 Loon
with Security Device

ELIZABETH II, UNCROWNED PORTRAIT, 2011

Date and Mint Mark	Description	Buying Price
2011	Parks Canada	1.00

Obv.

30th Anniv.
Loon Dollar

2012 Grey Cup

2012 Lucky Loonie
with Security Device

ELIZABETH II, UNCROWNED PORTRAIT, 2012

Date and Mint Mark	Description	Buying Price
1987-2012	30th Anniv. Loon Dollar	1.00

2014 Lucky Loonie

ELIZABETH II, UNCROWNED PORTRAIT, SECURITY DEVICE, 2012-2015

Date and Mint Mark	Description	Buying Price
2012	Loon, Security Device	1.00
2012	Grey Cup, Security Device	1.00
2012	Lucky Loonie, Security Device	1.00
2013	Loon, Security Device	1.00
2014	Loon, Security Device	1.00
2014	Lucky Loonie, Security Device	1.00
2015	Loon, Security Device	1.00

TWO DOLLAR COINS

ELIZABETH II, DIADEMED PORTRAIT 1996 - 1998

Date and Mint Mark	Description	Buying Price
1996		2.00
1997		2.00
1998		2.00

ELIZABETH II, DIADEMED PORTRAIT, 2001 - 2003

Date and Mint Mark	Description	Buying Price
2001		2.00
1952-2002	Double Date	2.00
2003		2.00

ELIZABETH II, DIADEMED PORTRAIT, 1999

Date and Mint Mark	Description	Buying Price
1999	Nunavut	2.00

ELIZABETH II, UNCROWNED PORTRAIT, 2003 - 2006

Date and Mint Mark	Description	Buying Price
2003		2.00
2004		2.00
2005		2.00
2006		2.00

ELIZABETH II, DIADEMED PORTRAIT, 2000

Date and Mint Mark	Description	Buying Price
2000	Polar Bears	2.00

Obv. 1996-2006	2006 10th Anniversary	Obv. 2011	2011 Boreal Forest

Obv. 1996-2006	2006 10th Anniversary "Churchill"	Obv. 2012	2012-2014 with Security Device

Security Device

Obv. 2007   Common Rev. 2006-2012

Obv. 2012   2012 HMS Shannon

Obv. 2008   2008 400th Anniversary Quebec City

ELIZABETH II, UNCROWNED PORTRAIT, 2006-2009

Date and Mint Mark	Description	Buying Price
2006	10th Anniv.	2.00
2006	10th Anniv. "Churchill"	2.00
2006		2.00
2007		2.00
2008		2.00
2008	400th Anniv. Quebec City	2.00
2009		2.00

ELIZABETH II, UNCROWNED PORTRAIT, LOGO, 2010 - 2014

Date and Mint Mark	Description	Buying Price
2010		2.00
2011		2.00
2011	Boreal Forest	2.00
2012		2.00
2012	Security Device	2.00
2012	HMS Shannon	2.00
2013	Security Device	2.00
2014	Security Device	2.00

ELIZABETH II, UNCROWNED PORTRAIT, LOGO, 2014

ELIZABETH II, UNCROWNED PORTRAIT, LOGO, 2015

Obv. 2014   2014 Wait For Me, Daddy

Obv. 2015   2015 Sir John A Macdonald

Date and Mint Mark	Description	Buying Price
2014	"Wait For Me, Daddy"	2.00

Date and Mint Mark	Description	Buying Price
2015	Sir John A. Macdonald	2.00
2015	Security Device	2.00

Note: For Collector varieties of the two dollar coins, see pages 89 and 90.

CIRCULATING GOLD COINS

SOVEREIGNS

FIVE DOLLARS

EDWARD VII 1908 - 1910

Date and Mint Mark	Buying VF Price
1908C	1,200.00
1909C	325.00
1910C	325.00

GEORGE V 1912 - 1914

Date and Mint Mark	Buying VF Price
1912	350.00
1913	350.00
1914	400.00

TEN DOLLARS

GEORGE V 1911 - 1919

Date and Mint Mark	Buying VF Price
1911C	325.00
1913C	350.00
1914C	350.00
1916C	10,000.00
1917C	325.00
1918C	325.00
1919C	325.00

GEORGE V 1912 - 1914

Date and Mint Mark	Buying VF Price
1912	700.00
1913	700.00
1914	700.00

IMPORTANT: Do not clean your coins. Coins should be handled carefully. Only experts should consider cleaning. If you are not an expert, the results can be disastrous.

COLLECTOR COINS

The numismatic department of the Royal Canadian Mint issued specially struck and packaged coins starting in 1954. The coins were issued for collectors and as a result are of high quality. The dealer buying prices listed below are for single coins and sets in their original packaging and condition. Coins or sets which have been mishandled or damaged are discounted from the prices listed. Beginning in 1971 the numismatic department of the Royal Canadian Mint issued silver dollars for collectors in two conditions, proof and uncirculated. Proof condition dollars were issued in black leatherette boxes while uncirculated dollars were issued in a clear plastic container.

ONE CENT

Date	Description	Buying Price
2003	Selectively gold plated	20.00

SILVER THREE CENTS

Date	Description	Buying Price
2001	3 Cent Beaver	5.00

SILVER FIVE CENTS

2000-2001
Common Obv.

Les Voltigeurs
de Québec

Royal Military
College of Canada

85th Anniv. Battle
for Vimy Ridge

Date	Description	Buying Price
2000	Les Voltigeurs de Québec	5.00
2001	Royal Military College Canada	5.00
2002	85th Anniv. Battle Vimy Ridge	10.00

60th Anniversary D-Day 1944-2004

60th Anniversary VE-Day 1945-2005

1945-2005
Selectively
gold plated

Date	Description	Buying Price
2004	60th Anniv. D-Day	25.00
2005	60th Anniv. VE-Day	10.00
2005	VE-Day, Gold plated	25.00

SILVER TEN CENTS

500th Anniv. Caboto's First Transatlantic Voyage

Date	Description	Buying Price
1997	Caboto	7.00

100th Anniv. Credit Unions in N.A., 2000

Int'l Year of the Volunteers, 2001

100th Anniv. Canadian Open Golf Chmpshp, 2004

Date	Description	Buying Price
2000	100th Anniv. Credit Unions	4.00
2001	Int'l Year of Volunteers	5.00
2004	Canadian Open Golf	6.00

TWENTY-FIVE CENTS
125TH ANNIVERSARY 1867-1992

For the complete 12-coin set of the 1867-1992, 125th Anniversary see page 29. The set was minted in both nickel and silver

January - New Brunswick

Date	Description	No. of Coins	Buying Price
1992	125th Anniversary silver proof set	13	50.00
1992	Single silver coin	1	4.00
1992	125 Anniversary nickel souvenier set	13	5.00

TWENTY-FIVE CENTS
1999 - 2000 MILLENNIUM

For the complete 24-coin set of the 1999-2000 millennium celebration see pages 30 and 31. The coins were issued in both nickel and silver.

January 1999

1999 Millennium Medallion

September 1999 Mule
Obverse has no denomination

November 1999 Mule
Obverse has no denomination

Date	Description	Buying Price
1999	12 coin set and 1999 medallion	5.00
1999	September, no denomination	50.00
1999	November, no denomination	50.00
1999	Medallion	1.00
1999	12 coin silver set	50.00
1999	Single silver coin	4.00

TWENTY-FIVE CENTS

2000 MILLENNIUM

January 2000, for complete set see pages 30-31.

2000 Royal Canadian Mint Medallion

2000 Mule
Coin Obverse with Medallion Obverse

Date	Description	Buying Price
2000	12-coin set, medallion	4.00
2000	Medallion	1.00
2000	Coin; medallion mule	200.00
2000	12-coin silver set	50.00
2000	Single silver coin	4.00

CANADA'S FIRST COLOURISED COIN

Obv. 2000-2003

Date	Description	Buying Price
2000	First colourised coin	5.00

Note: 2009 coin illustrated smaller than actual size

CANADA DAY SERIES

Canada Day 2000   Canada Day 2001

Canada Day 2002   Canada Day 2003

Obv. 2004-2008   Canada Day, 2004

Moose 2004   Canada Day 2005

Canada Day 2006   Canada Day 2007

Canada Day 2008   Canada Day 2009

CANADA DAY SERIES (cont.)

Date	Description	Buying Price
2000	Canada Day 2000	25.00
2001P	Canada Day 2001	5.00
2002P	Canada Day 2002	5.00
2003P	Canada Day 2003	5.00
2004P	Canada Day 2004	5.00
2004P	Moose 2004	5.00
2005P	Canada Day 2005	5.00
2006P	Canada Day 2006	5.00
2007	Canada Day 2007	5.00
2008	Canada Day 2008	5.00
2009	Canada Day 2009	5.00

CHRISTMAS DAY SERIES

2004
Santa Claus

2005
Christmas Stocking

2006
Santa in Sleigh

2007
Christmas Tree

2008
Santa

2009 Santa and
Maple Leaves

Date	Description	Buying Price
2004	Santa Claus	12.00
2005	Christmas Stocking	5.00
2006	Santa in Sleigh and Reindeer	5.00
2007	Christmas Tree	5.00
2008	Santa	5.00
2009	Santa Claus and Maple Leaves	5.00
2010	Santa Claus and Christmas Tree	5.00

2004 Poppy

2005 Poppy   2005 Liberation

Date	Description	Buying Price
2004	Poppy, Silver	12.00
2005P	Poppy, Nickel*	5.00
2005	Liberation, Silver	30.00

QUEBEC WINTER CARNIVAL

Date	Description	Buying Price
2006P	Quebec Winter Carnival	5.00

BREAST CANCER AWARENESS

Date	Description	Buying Price
2006P	Breast Cancer Awareness*	5.00

Note: * These coins were encased in a plastic bookmark.

NHL HOCKEY SERIES (Giftware Sets)

2005-2006 HOCKEY SEASON

Common Obv.

Montreal Canadiens

Ottawa Senators

Toronto Maple Leafs

2006-2007 HOCKEY SEASON

Common Obv.

Calgary Flames

Edmonton Oilers

Montreal Canadiens

Ottawa Senators

Toronto Maple Leafs

Vancouver Canucks

Date	Description	Buying Price
2006P	Montreal Canadiens	7.00
2006P	Ottawa Senators	7.00
2006P	Toronto Maple Leafs	7.00
2007	Calgary Flames	7.00
2007	Edmonton Oilers	7.00
2007	Montreal Canadiens	7.00
2007	Ottawa Senators	7.00
2007	Toronto Maple Leafs	7.00
2007	Vancouver Canucks	7.00

QUEEN ELIZABETH II COMMEMORATIVES

2006 80th Birthday
Queen Elizabeth II

2007 60th Wedding Anniversary
Queen Elizabeth II /Prince Philip

Date	Description	Buying Price
2006	80th Birthday Queen Elizabeth II	10.00
2007	60th Wedding Anniversary	10.00

COLOURISED OCCASIONS SERIES (Giftware Sets)

OCCASIONS – 2007-2010

2007 Baby Set

2007 Birthday Set

2008 Oh! Canada Set

2008 Wedding Set

2007 Congratulations Set

2007 Oh! Canada Set

2009 Baby Set

2009 Oh! Canada Set

2007 Wedding Set

2008 Baby Set

2010 Baby Set

2010 Oh! Canada Set

2008 Birthday Set

2008 Congratulations Set

2010 Wedding Set

Date	Description	Buying Price	Date	Description	Buying Price
2007	Baby / Rattle	7.00	2008	Oh! Canada / Flag	7.00
2007	Birthday / Balloons	7.00	2008	Wedding / Cake	7.00
2007	Congratulations / Fireworks	7.00	2009	Baby / Teddy Bear, Moon	7.00
2007	Oh! Canada / Maple Leaf	7.00	2009	Oh! Canada / Four Maple Leaves	7.00
2007	Wedding / Bouquet	7.00	2010	Baby / Carriage	7.00
2008	Baby / Teddy Bear	7.00	2010	Oh! Canada / Three Maple Leaves	7.00
2008	Birthday / Party Hat	7.00	2010	Wedding / Heart and Roses	7.00
2008	Congratulations / Trophy	7.00			

COLOURISED OCCASIONS SERIES (Giftware)

CARDS WITH COINS - 2009-2012

OCCASIONS - 2011-2012

2009 Birthday Card

2009 Congratulations

2011 Baby Set

2011 Birthday Set

2009 Thank You Card

2009 Wedding Card

2011 Holiday Set

2011 Oh! Canada Set

2010 Birthday Card

2010 Congratulations

2011 Wedding Set

2012 Baby Set

2010 Thank You Card

2011 Tooth Fairy

2012 Birthday Set

2012 Holiday Set

2012 Tooth Fairy

2012 Oh! Canada Set

2012 Wedding Set

Date	Description	Buying Price	Date	Description	Buying Price
2009	Birthday / Balloons & Streamers	7.00	2011	Baby / Baby's Feet	7.00
2009	Congratulations / Fireworks	7.00	2011	Birthday / Balloons	7.00
2009	Thank You / Stylized Flower	7.00	2011	Holiday Set / Peace and Joy	7.00
2009	Wedding / Doves & Rings	7.00	2011	Oh! Canada / Maple Leaf	7.00
2010	Birthday / Gift Box	7.00	2011	Wedding / Wedding Rings	7.00
2010	Congratulations / Stars	7.00	2012	Baby / Mobiles	7.00
2010	Thank You / Flowers	7.00	2012	Birthday / Ice Cream Cone	7.00
2011	Tooth Fairy	7.00	2013	Holiday / Tree Ornaments	7.00
2012	Tooth Fairy	7.00	2012	Oh! Canada / Maple Leaves	7.00
			2012	Wedding / Wedding Rings	7.00

OCCASIONS SERIES (Giftware)

OCCASIONS – 2013

2013 Baby Set

2013 Birthday Set

2013 Holiday Set

2013 Oh! Canada Set

2013 Wedding Set

Date	Description	Buying Price	Date	Description	Buying Price
2013	Baby / Baby's Feet	7.00	2013	Oh! Canada / Maple Leaf	7.00
2013	Birthday / Cake	7.00	2013	Wedding / Wedding Rings	7.00
2013	Holiday / Holly Wreath	7.00			

BIRD SERIES

2007 Ruby-Throated Hummingbird

2007 Red-Breasted Nuthatch

2008 Downy Woodpecker

2008 Northern Cardinal

2010 Goldfinch

2010 Blue Jay

2011 Black-capped Chickadee

2011 Barn Swallow

2012 Rose-Breasted Grosbeak

2012 Evening Grosbeak

2013 American Robin

2013 Barn Owl

2014 Eastern Meadowlark

2014 Scarlet Tanager

Date	Description	Buying Price	Date	Description	Buying Price
2007	Ruby-Throated Hummingbird	40.00	2011	Barn Swallow	25.00
2007	Red-Breasted Nuthatch	200.00	2012	Rose-Breasted Grosbeak	15.00
2008	Downy Woodpecker	75.00	2012	Evening Grosbeak	15.00
2008	Northern Cardinal	150.00	2013	American Robin	15.00
2010	Goldfinch	75.00	2013	Barn Owl	15.00
2010	Blue Jay	50.00	2014	Eastern Meadowlark	15.00
2011	Black-capped Chickadee	30.00	2014	Scarlet Tanager	15.00

CANADIAN COMMEMORATIVES

2008 Tomb of the
Unknown Soldier

2008 Anne of Green Gables©

2009 Notre-Dame-Du-Saguenay

Date	Description	Buying Price	Date	Description	Buying Price
2008	Tomb of the Unknown Soldier	10.00	2009	Notre-Dame-Du-Saguenay	10.00
2008	Anne of Green Gables©	10.00			

CANADIAN MYTHICAL CREATURES

2011 Sasquatch

2011 Memphré

2011 Mishepishu

Date	Description	Buying Price	Date	Description	Buying Price
2011	Sasquatch	12.00	2011	Mishepishu	12.00
2011	Memphré	12.00			

OUR LEGENDARY NATURE SERIES (Silver)

2011 Common Obv.

2011 Wood Bison

2011 Orca Whale

2011 Peregrine Falcon

Date	Description	Buying Price	Date	Description	Buying Price
2011	Wood Bison (painted)	12.00	2011	Peregrine Falcon (painted)	12.00
2011	Orca Whale (painted)	12.00			

GARDEN FLOWERS AND INSECTS

2011 Tulip With Ladybug

2012 Aster with Bumble Bee

2013 Purple Coneflower and Eastern Tailed Blue Butterfly

Date	Description	Buying Price	Date	Description	Buying Price
2011	Tulip With Ladybug	15.00	2013	Purple Coneflower/Butterfly	10.00
2012	Aster with Bumble Bee	12.00	2014	Water-lily and Leopard Frog	10.00

COMMEMORATIVE ISSUES 2011-2012

2011 The Wedding Celebration

2011 75th Anniversary CBC/Radio Canada

2011 Wayne Gretzky

2012 RMS Titanic

2012 Calgary Stmpede

2012 Canadian Coast Guard

Date	Description	Buying Price	Date	Description	Buying Price
2011	The Wedding Celebration	10.00	2012	RMS Titanic	15.00
2011	75th Anniv. CBC/Radio Canada	10.00	2012	100th Anniv. Calgary Stampede	10.00
2011	Wayne Gretzky	15.00	2012	50th Anniv. Can. Coast Guard	10.00

CANADIAN FOOTBALL LEAGUE SERIES

British Columbia Lions

Calgary Stampeders

Edmonton Eskimos

Hamilton Tiger Cats

Montreal Alouettes

Saskatchewan Roughriders

Toronto Argonauts

Winnipeg Blue Bombers

Date	Description	Buying Price	Date	Description	Buying Price
2012	British Columbia Lions	12.00	2012	Montreal Alouettes	12.00
2012	Calgary Stampeders	12.00	2012	Saskatchewan Roughriders	12.00
2012	Edmonton Eskimos	12.00	2012	Toronto Argonauts	12.00
2012	Hamilton Tiger Cats	12.00	2012	Winnpeg Blue Bombers	12.00

PREHISTORIC CREATURES SERIES

2012 Pachyrhinosaurus Lakustai

Quetzalcoatlus

2013 Tylosaurus Pembinensis

Tiktaalik

DUCKS OF CANADA SERIES

Mallard

Wood Duck

Northern Pintail

Harlequin Duck

Date	Description	Buying Price
2012	Pachyrhinosaurus Lakustai	25.00
2013	Quetzalcoatlus	15.00
2013	Tylosaurus Pembinensis	15.00
2014	Tiktaalik	15.00

Date	Description	Buying Price
2013	Mallard	15.00
2013	Wood Duck	15.00
2014	Northern Pintail	15.00
2014	Harlequin Duck	15.00
2015	Cinnamon Teal	15.00

CANADIAN HOCKEY LEAGUE SERIES

Calgary Flames

Edmonton Oilers

Montreal Canadiens

Ottawa Senators

Toronto Maple Leafs

Vancouver Canucks

Winnipeg Jets

Date	Description	Buying Price	Date	Description	Buying Price
2014	Calgary Flames	12.00	2014	Toronto Maple Leafs	12.00
2014	Edmonton Oilers	12.00	2014	Vancouver Canucks	12.00
2014	Montreal Canadiens	12.00	2014	Winnipeg Jets	12.00
2014	Ottawa Senatorss	12.00			

PROOF SILVER FIFTY CENTS
WILD LIFE SERIES

Atlantic Puffin

Whooping Crane

Gray Jays

White Tailed Ptarmigans

Date	Description	Buying Price
1995	Atlantic Puffins	7.00
1995	Whooping Crane	7.00

Date	Description	Buying Price
1995	Gray Jays	7.00
1995	White Tailed Ptarmigans	7.00

Moose Calf

Wood Ducklings

Cougar Kittens

Black Bear Cubs

Date	Description	Buying Price
1996	Moose Calf	7.00
1996	Wood Ducklings	7.00

Date	Description	Buying Price
1996	Cougar Kittens	7.00
1996	Black Bear Cubs	7.00

Newfoundland

Nova Scotia Duck
Tolling Retriever

Labrador Retriever

Canadian Eskimo Dog

Date	Description	Buying Price
1997	Newfoundland	7.00
1997	Nova Scotia Duck Tolling Retriever	7.00

Date	Description	Buying Price
1997	Labrador Retriever	7.00
1997	Canadian Eskimo Dog	7.00

PROOF SILVER FIFTY CENTS
WILD LIFE SERIES

Killer Whale

Humpback Whale

Beluga Whale

Blue Whale

Date	Description	Buying Price
1998	Killer Whale	7.00
1998	Humpback Whale	7.00

Date	Description	Buying Price
1998	Beluga Whale	7.00
1998	Blue Whale	7.00

Tonkinese · Lynx

Cymric · Cougar

Date	Description	Buying Price
1999	Tonkinese	9.00
1999	Lynx	9.00

Date	Description	Buying Price
1999	Cymric	9.00
1999	Cougar	9.00

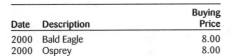

Bald Eagle · Osprey

Great Horned Owl · Red-Tailed Hawk

Date	Description	Buying Price
2000	Bald Eagle	8.00
2000	Osprey	8.00

Date	Description	Buying Price
2000	Great Horned Owl	8.00
2000	Red-Tailed Hawk	8.00

PROOF SILVER FIFTY CENTS
SPORTS SERIES

Figure Skating Skiing Soccer Auto Racing

Date	Description	Buying Price	Date	Description	Buying Price
1998	Figure Skating	7.00	1998	Soccer	7.00
1998	Skiing	7.00	1998	Auto Racing	7.00

Golf Yacht Race Football Basketball

Date	Description	Buying Price	Date	Description	Buying Price
1999	Golf	7.00	1999	Football	7.00
1999	Yacht Race	7.00	1999	Basketball	7.00

Hockey Curling Steeplechase Bowling

Date	Description	Buying Price	Date	Description	Buying Price
2000	Hockey	7.00	2000	Steeplechase	7.00
2000	Curling	7.00	2000	Bowling	7.00

PROOF SILVER FIFTY CENTS
CANADIAN FESTIVALS SERIES

Quebec Winter
Carnival (Quebec)

Toonik Tyme
(Nunavut)

Newfoundland and
Labrador Folk Festival
(Newfoundland)

Festival of Fathers
(Prince Edward Island)

Annapolis Valley
Blossom Festival
(Nova Scotia)

Stratford Festival of
Canada (Ontario)

Folklorama
(Manitoba)

Calgary Stampede
(Alberta)

Squamish Days
Logger Sports
(British Columbia)

Yukon Festival
(Yukon)

Back to Batoche
(Saskatchewan)

Great Northern
Arts Festival
(Northwest Territories)

Festival Acadien
de Caraquet
(New Brunswick)

Date	Description	Price	Date	Description	Price
2001	Québec	7.00	2002	Alberta	7.00
2001	Nunavut	7.00	2002	British Columbia	7.00
2001	Newfoundland	7.00	2003	Yukon	7.00
2001	Prince Edward Island	7.00	2003	Saskatchewan	7.00
2002	Nova Scotia	7.00	2003	Northwest Territories	7.00
2002	Ontario	7.00	2003	New Brunswick	7.00
2002	Manitoba	7.00	2001-03	Set Can. Festivals (13 coins)	100.00

PROOF SILVER FIFTY CENTS
CANADIAN FOLKLORE AND LEGENDS SERIES

The Sled

The Maiden's Cave

Les Petits Sauteux

The Pig That Wouldn't

Shoemaker in Heaven

Le Vaisseau Fantome

Date	Description	Price	Date	Description	Price
2001	The Sled	8.00	2002	The Pig That Wouldn't	8.00
2001	The Maiden's Cave	8.00	2002	Shoemaker in Heaven	8.00
2001	Les Petits Sauteux	8.00	2002	Le Vaisseau Fantome	8.00

FLOWER SERIES

Golden Tulip Festival

Golden Daffodil

Golden Easter Lily

Golden Rose

Golden Daisy

Golden Forget-Me-Not

Date	Description	Price	Date	Description	Price
2002	Golden Tulip Festival	35.00	2005	Golden Rose	15.00
2003	Golden Daffodil	15.00	2006	Golden Daisy	20.00
2004	Golden Easter Lily	20.00	2007	Golden Forget-Me-Not	35.00

PROOF SILVER FIFTY CENTS
COAT OF ARMS OF CANADA

Kruger-Gray 1953

Shingles 1954-1958

Shingles 1959-1996

Bursey-Sabourin
1997-2010

Date	Description	Buying Price	Date	Description	Buying Price
2004	Kruger-Gray, 1953	8.00	2004	Shingles 1959-1996	8.00
2004	Shingles, 1954-1958	8.00	2004	Bursey-Sabourin, 1997-2010	8.00

CANADIAN BUTTERFLY COLLECTION

Canadian Tiger Swallowtail

Canadian Clouded Sulpher

Monarch

Spangled Fritillary

Short-tailed Swallowtail

Silvery Blue

Date	Description	Buying Price	Date	Description	Buying Price
2004	Canadian Tiger Swallowtail	25.00	2005	Spangled Fritillary	25.00
2004	Canadian Clouded Sulpher	25.00	2006	Short-tailed Swallowtail	25.00
2005	Monarch	25.00	2006	Silvery Blue	25.00

FIFTY CENTS
QUEST FOR PEACE AND FREEDOM DURING SECOND WORLD WAR

Battle of Britain

Liberation of Netherlands

Conquest of Sicily

Battle of the Scheldt

Raid on Dieppe

Battle of the Atlantic

Date	Description	Buying Price	Date	Description	Buying Price
2005	Battle of Britain	15.00	2005	Battle of the Scheldt	15.00
2005	Liberation of Netherlands	15.00	2005	Raid on Dieppe	15.00
2005	Conquest of Sicily	15.00	2005	Battle of the Atlantic	15.00

HOCKEY LEGENDS

Jean Beliveau

Guy Lafleur

Jacques Plante

Maurice Richard

Johnny Bower

Tim Horton

Darryl Sittler

Dave Keon

Date	Description	Buying Price	Date	Description	Buying Price
2005	Jean Beliveau	15.00	2005	Johnny Bower	15.00
2005	Guy Lafleur	15.00	2005	Tim Horton	15.00
2005	Jacques Plante	15.00	2005	Darryl Sittler	15.00
2005	Maurice Richard	15.00	2005	Dave Keon	15.00

FIFTY CENTS
NHL HOCKEY SERIES

2008-2009 NHL SEASON

Calgary Flames

Edmonton Oilers

Montreal Canadiens

Ottawa Senators

Toronto Maple Leafs

Vancouver Canucks

MONTREAL CANADIENS CENTENNIAL

Canadiens Home Jersey

1945-1946 Road Jersey

1915-1916 Le Club de
Hockey Canadiens

1912-1913 "CAC"

1910-1911 Club
Athletique Canadien

1909-1910 Club de
Hockey le Canadien

Date	Description	Buying Price
2009	Calgary Flames	7.00
2009	Edmonton Oilers	7.00
2009	Montreal Canadiens	7.00
009	Ottawa Senators	7.00
2009	Toronto Maple Leafs	7.00
2009	Vancouver Canucks	7.00

Date	Description	Buying Price
2009	Monteal Canadiens Home Jersey	7.00
2009	1945-1946 Road Jersey	7.00
2009	1915-1916 Le Club de Hockey Can.	7.00
2009	1912-1913 "CAC"	7.00
2009	1910-1911 Club Athletiqu Can.	7.00
2009	1909-1910 Club de Hockey Can.	7.00

Note: Coins illustrated smaller than actual size.

FIFTY CENTS
NHL HOCKEY SERIES

2009-2010 NHL SEASON

Calgary Flames

Edmonton Oilers

Montreal Canadiens

Ottawa Senators

Toronto Maple Leafs

Vancouver Canucks

Date	Description	Buying Price	Date	Description	Buying Price
2009-2010	Calgary Flames	7.00	2009-2010	Ottawa Senators	7.00
2009-2010	Edmonton Oilers	7.00	2009-2010	Toronto Maple Leafs	7.00
2009-2010	Montreal Canadiens	7.00	2009-2010	Vancouver Canucks	7.00

HOLIDAY LENTICULAR SERIES

2007 Holiday Ornaments   2008 Holiday Snowman

2009 Holiday Toy Train   2010 Santa Claus and the
Red-Nosed Reindeer

2011 Gifts From Santa   2012 Santa's Magical Visit

2013 Snowman   2014 Christmas Tree

Date	Description	Buying Price
2007	Holiday Ornaments	15.00
2008	Holiday Snowman	15.00
2009	Holiday Toy Train	15.00
2010	Santa Claus / Reindeer	15.00
2011	Gifts From Santa	15.00
2012	Santa's Magical Visit	15.00
2013	Snowman	15.00
2014	Christmas Tree	15.00

Note: Coins illustrated smalled than actual size.

TRIANGULAR COIN SERIES

2008 Milk Delivery

Date	Description	Buying Price
2008	Milk Delivery	20.00

2009 Six String Nation Guitar

Date	Description	Buying Price
2009	Six String Nation Guitar	20.00

VANCOUVER 2010 MASCOTS – FIFTY CENTS

Miga Ice Hockey

Quatchi Ice Hockey

Sumi Ice Sledge Hockey

Quatchi / Miga
Figure Skating

Quatchi / Miga
Bobsleigh

Miga Ariels

Miga Skeleton

Quatchi Snowboard Cross

Miga Alpine Skiing

Sumi Paralympic
Alpine Skiing

Quatchi Paralell
Giant Slalom

Miga Speed Skating

Date	Description	Buying Price	Date	Description	Buying Price
2010	Miga Ice Hockey	4.00	2010	Miga Skeleton	4.00
2010	Quatchi Ice Hockey	4.00	2010	Quatchi Snowboard Cross	4.00
2010	Sumi Ice Sledge Hockey	4.00	2010	Miga Alpine Skiing	4.00
2010	Quatchi / Miga Figure Skating	4.00	2010	Sumi Paralympic Alpine Skiing	4.00
2010	Quatchi / Miga Bobsleigh	4.00	2010	Quatchi Paralell Giant Slalom	4.00
2010	Miga Ariels	4.00	2010	Miga Speed Skating	4.00

Note: Coins illustrated smaller than actual size.

DINOSAUR EXHIBIT SERIES

Daspletosaurus Torosus

Albertosaurus

Sinosauropteryx

Date	Description	Buying Price	Date	Description	Buying Price
2010	Daspletosaurus Torosus	10.00	2010	Sinosauropteryx	10.00
2010	Albertosaurus	10.00			

CANADIAN FIFTY CENT COMMEMORATIVES 2011-2014

2011 Winnipeg Jets

2012 Royal Cypher,
Queen's Diamond Jubilee

2012 R.M.S. Titanic

2013 Superman

2013 Canadian Tiger Swallowtail

2014 100 Blessings of Good Fortune

Date	Description	Buying Price	Date	Description	Buying Price
2011	Winnipeg Jets	7.00	2013	Superman	20.00
2012	Royal Cypher, Queen's Dia. Jubilee	10.00	2013	Canadian Tiger Swallowtail	15.00
2012	R.M.S. Titanic	45.00	2014	100 Blessings of Good Fortune	20.00

SILVER PROOF-LIKE DOLLARS

Single dollars, in either cellophane or pliofilm packaging, were issued by the Royal Canadian Mint for collectors. Illustrations of these dollars can be found on page 41.

Date	Description	Buying Price	Date	Description	Buying Price
1954	Voyageur	250.00	1959	Voyageur	15.00
1955	Voyageur	150.00	1960	Voyageur	10.00
1955	Arnprior	225.00	1961	Voyageur	10.00
1956	Voyageur	100.00	1962	Voyageur	10.00
1957	Voyageur	60.00	1963	Voyageur	10.00
1958	British Columbia	40.00	1964	Charlottetown	10.00

CASED NICKEL DOLLARS

1970 Manitoba

1971 British Columbia

1973 Prince Edward Island

1974 Winnipeg

1982 Constitution

1984 Jacques Cartier

Date	Description	Buying Price	Date	Description	Buying Price
1970	Manitoba	1.25	1975	Voyageur	1.25
1971	British Columbia	1.25	1976	Voyageur	1.25
1972	Voyageur	1.25	1982	Constitution	2.00
1973	Prince Edward Island	1.25	1984	Jacques Cartier	2.00
1974	Winnipeg	1.25			

Note: Coins must be as issued in clam style Mint cases.

CASED SILVER DOLLARS

1971 British Columbia   1973 R.C.M.P.   1974 Winnipeg Centennial

1975 Calgary Stampede   1976 Library of Parliament   1977 Silver Jubilee

1978 Commonwealth Games   1979 Griffon Tricentennial   1980 Arctic Territories

Date	Description	Buying Price	Date	Description	Buying Price
1971	British Columbia Centennial (SP)	6.50	1976	Library of Parliament (SP)	6.50
1972	Voyageur (SP)	6.50	1977	Silver Jubilee (SP)	6.50
1973	R.C.M.P. (SP)	6.50	1978	Commonwealth Games (SP)	6.50
1974	Winnipeg Centennial (SP)	6.50	1979	Griffon Tricentennial (SP)	6.50
1975	Calgary Stampede (SP)	6.50	1980	Arctic Territories Centennial (SP)	8.00

Note: SP - Specimen; PR Proof; UNC - Brillian Uncirculated. All silver coin finishes.

CASED SILVER DOLLARS

1981 Trans-Canada Railway

1982 Regina Centennial

1983 World University Games

1984 Toronto Sesquicentennial

1985 National Parks Centannial

1986 Vancouver Centennial

1987 John Davis Strait

1988 Saint-Maurice Ironworks

1989 MacKenzie River

Date	Description	Buying Price	Date	Description	Buying Price
1981	Trans-Canada Railway (PR)	6.50	1985	National Parks Centennial (UNC)	6.50
1981	Trans-Canada Railway (UNC)	6.50	1986	Vancouver Centennial (PR)	6.50
1982	Regina Centennial (PR)	6.50	1986	Vancouver Centennial (UNC)	6.50
1982	Regina Centennial (UNC)	6.50	1987	John Davis Strait (PR)	6.50
1983	World University Games (PR)	6.50	1987	John Davis Strait (UNC)	6.50
1983	World University Games (UNC)	6.50	1988	Sainte-Maurice Ironworks (PR)	6.50
1984	Toronto Sesquicentennial (PR)	6.50	1988	Sainte-Maurice Ironworks (UNC)	6.50
1984	Toronto Sesquicentennial (UNC)	6.50	1989	MacKenzie River (PR)	7.50
1985	National Parks Centennial (PR)	6.50	1989	MacKenzie River (UNC)	6.50

CASED SILVER DOLLARS

1990 Henry Kelsey Tricentennial

1991 Frontenac

1992 Kingston Stagecoach

1993 Stanley Cup

1994 R.C.M.P. Northern
Dog Team Patrol

1995 325th Anniv. Founding
of Hudson's Bay Co.

1996 200th Anniversary
John McIntosh

1997 Canada/Russia Hockey

1997 Flying Loon

Date	Description	Buying Price	Date	Description	Buying Price
1990	Henry Kelsey (PR)	8.50	1994	R.C.M.P. (PR)	13.00
1990	Henry Kelsey (UNC)	8.50	1994	R.C.M.P. (UNC)	13.00
1991	Frontenac (PR)	8.50	1995	Hudson's Bay Co. (PR)	13.00
1991	Frontenac (UNC)	8.50	1995	Hudson's Bay Co. (UNC)	13.00
1992	Kingston Stagecoach (PR)	13.00	1996	John McIntosh (PR)	14.00
1992	Kingston Stagecoach (UNC)	13.00	1996	John McIntosh (UNC)	13.00
1993	Stanley Cup (PR)	14.00	1997	Canada/Russia Hockey (PR)	14.00
1993	Stanley Cup (UNC)	13.00	1997	Canada/Russia Hockey (UNC)	13.00
			1997	Flying Loon (PR)	50.00

CASED SILVER DOLLARS

1998 125th Anniversary RCMP

1999 225th Anniv. Juan Perez

1999 Int'l Year Older Persons

2000 Voyage of Discovery

2001 50th Anniversary
National Ballet of Canada

2001 90th Anniversary
Canada's 1911 Silver Dollar

2002 50th Anniv. Elizabeth II's
Accession to the Throne

2002 Queen Mother

2003 Cobalt

Date	Description	Buying Price
1998	RCMP (PR)	13.00
1998	RCMP (UNC)	13.00
1999	Juan Perez (PR)	13.00
1999	Juan Perez (UNC)	13.00
1999	Int'l Year Older Persons (PR)	15.00
2000	Voyage of Discovery (PR)	13.00
2000	Voyage of Discovery (UNC)	13.00

Date	Description	Buying Price
2001	National Ballet of Canada (PR)	13.00
2001	National Ballet of Canada (UNC)	13.00
2001	90th Anniv. 1911 Silver Dollar (PR)	35.00
2002	50th Anniv. Accession (PR)	13.00
2002	50th Anniv. Accession (UNC)	13.00
2002	Queen Mother (PR)	100.00
2003	Cobalt (PR)	13.00
2003	Cobalt (Unc)	13.00

Note: **(PR)** Proof condition one dollar silver coins are issued in a black leatherette case.
(UNC) UNC condition one dollar silver coins are issued in a clear plastic case.

CASED SILVER DOLLARS

2003 50th Anniv. Coronation

2004 First French Settlement

2004 "Poppy" Armistice

2005 40th Anniv. Canadian Flag

2006 150th Anniv. Victoria Cross

2007 Medal of Bravery

2007 Thayendanegna

2007 Celebration of the Arts

2008 Quebec City

Date	Description	Buying Price	Date	Description	Buying Price
2003	Coronation (PR)	15.00	2006	Victoria Cross (Unc)	15.00
2004	First French Settlement (PR)	15.00	2006	Victoria Cross (Gold Plated)	50.00
2004	First French Settlement (Unc)	13.00	2006	Medal of Bravery (PR)	30.00
2004	First French Settle, Privy Mark	40.00	2006	Medal of Bravery (En.)	75.00
2004	Lucky Loon (PR)	25.00	2007	Thayendanegea (PR)	25.00
2004	"Poppy" Armistice (PR)	30.00	2007	Thayendanegea (Unc)	15.00
2005	40th Anniv. Can. Flag (PR)	15.00	2007	Thayendanegea (En.)	75.00
2005	40th Anniv. Can. Flag (Unc)	13.00	2007	Celebration of the Arts (PR)	45.00
2005	40th Anniv. Can. Flag (En.)	125.00	2008	Quebec City (PR)	25.00
2006	Victoria Cross (PR)	25.00	2008	Quebec City (Unc)	15.00

CASED SILVER DOLLARS

2008 RCM 100th Anniv.

2008 "Poppy" Armistice

2009 Flight in Canada

2009 Montreal Canadiens

2010 The Sun

2010 Navy, 100th Anniv.

2010 75th Anniv. Voyaguer Dollar

2010 Enamelled Poppy

2011 100th Anniv. Parks Canada

Date	Description	Buying Price	Date	Description	Buying Price
2008	RCM 100th Anniv.	75.00	2010	Navy, 100th Anniv. (PR)	20.00
2008	"Poppy" Armistice (PR)	75.00	2010	Navy, 100th Anniv. (Unc)	20.00
2009	Flight in Canada (PR)	25.00	2010	75th An. Voyaguer Dollar (PR)	50.00
2009	Flight in Canada (Unc)	18.00	2010	Enamelled Poppy (PR)	100.00
2009	Montreal Canadiens (PR)	100.00	2011	100th Anniv. Parks Canada (PR)	27.00
2010	The Sun (En.)	125.00	2011	100th Anniv. Parks Canada (Unc)	22.00

Note: (PR) Proof; (Unc) Uncirculated; (En.) Enamelled; (Cr) Circulation

CASED SILVER DOLLARS

2011 100th Anniv.
1911 Silver Dollar

2012 200th Anniv. War of 1812

2012 Two Loons

2012 100 Years of the
Calgary Stampede

2012 The 100th Grey Cup

2013 100th Anniversary of the
Canadian Arctic Expedition

2013 250th Anniv. of the
end of the Seven Years War

2013 60th Anniv. of the Korean
Armistice Agreement

2014 100th Anniv, Declaration
of the First World War

Date	Description	Buying Price	Date	Description	Buying Price
2011	100th Anniv. 1911 Silver Dollar	35.00	2013	End of Seven Years War (PR)	35.00
2012	200th Anniv. War of 1812 (PR)	30.00	2013	60th Anniv. Korean Armistice (PR)	30.00
2012	200th Anniv. War of 1812 (Unc)	25.00	2014	100th Ann. Declaration WWI (PR)	30.00
2012	Two Loons (PR)	75.00	2014	100th Ann. Declaration WWI (Unc)	25.00
2012	Calgary Stampede (PR)	50.00	2014	7th Anniv. Declaration WWII (PR)	35.00
2012	100th Grey Cup (PR)	40.00	2015	Canadian Flag (PR)	30.00
2013	Can. Arctic Expedition (PR)	35.00	2015	Canadian Flag (Unc)	25.00
2013	Can. Arctic Expedition (Unc)	25.00			

LOON STYLE STERLING SILVER PROOF DOLLARS

2004 Olympic Loon   2006 Loon Settling   2006 Lullaby Loonie   2006 Snowflake

2007 Baby Rattle   2007 "ABC" Building Blocks   2007 Loon   2008 Loon

2008 Loon Dance   2010 Reverse Anticipating the Games   2012 25th Anniv. 1987-2012   2012 25th Anniv. Gold Plated

2012 25th Anniv. of the Loonie   2012 25th Anniv. of the Lucky Loonie   2013 Loon Gold Plated Proof   2014 Lucky Loonie

Date	Description	Buying Price	Date	Description	Buying Price
2004	Olympic Loon (PR)	35.00	2008	Loon Dance (PR)	20.00
2006	Loon Settling (PR)	25.00	2010	Anticipating the Games (PR)	25.00
2006	Lullaby Loonie (PR)	100.00	2012	25th Anniv. Loon (PR)	20.00
2006	Snowflake (PR)	25.00	2012	25th Anniv. Gold Plated (PR)	40.00
2007	Baby Rattle (PR)	35.00	2012	25th Anniv., Loonie (PR)	20.00
2007	"ABC" Building Blocks (PR)	200.00	2012	25th Anniv., Lucky Loonie (PR)	20.00
2007	Loon (PR)	25.00	2013	Loon, Gold plated (PR)	20.00
2008	Loon (PR)	25.00	2014	Lucky Loonie (PR)	20.00

Note: The silver loon dollars were not issued for circulation. They were sold by the Mint, individually or in sets.

NICKEL-BRONZE DOLLARS

1987 Loon	1992 125th Anniv. of Canada	1994 Remembrance	1995 Peacekeeping
1997 Flying Loon	2002 15th Anniv. Loon	2002 Centre Ice	2004 Canada Goose
2004 Elusive Loon	2005 Tufted Puffin	2006 Snowy Owl	2007 Trumpeter Swan
2008 Loon Dance	2008 Common Eider	2009 Great Blue Heron	2009 Monteal Canadiens

Date	Description	Buying Price	Date	Description	Buying Price
1987	Loon (PR)	4.00	2004	Elusive Loon (SP)	20.00
1992	125th Anniv. of Canada (PR)	4.00	2005	Tufted Puffin (SP)	30.00
1994	Remembrance (PR)	4.00	2006	Snowy Owl (SP)	25.00
1995	Peacekeeping (PR)	4.00	2007	Trumpeter Swan (SP)	25.00
1997	Flying Loon (SP)	10.00	2008	Loon Dance (Cr)	25.00
2002	15th Anniv. Loon Dollar (SP)	15.00	2008	Common Eider (SP)	25.00
2002	Centre Ice (PR)	12.00	2009	Great Blue Heron (SP)	25.00
2004	Canada Goose (SP)	20.00	2009	Montreal Canadiens (Cr)	5.00

Note: The nickel-bronze collector dollars of 1992-2009 were issued singly or in Specimen or Proof sets.

NICKEL-BRONZE DOLLARS (cont.)

2010 Northern Harrier

2010 Vanvcouver
2010 Olympics

2010 Cananadian Navy
Gold plated

2010 Sask. Roughriders
Gold Plated

2011 Great Grey Owl

2012 25th Anniv. Loon

2012 25th Anniv. Loon
Silver plated bronze

2013 Blue-Winged Teal

2014 Ferruginous Hawk

2015 Blue Jay

Date	Description	Buying Price	Date	Description	Buying Price
2010	Northern Harrier (SP)	10.00	2012	25th An. Loon Dollar, Silver plated	10.00
2010	Vancouver 2010 Olympics (Cr)	10.00	2012	25th An. Loon Dollar, Gold plated	10.00
2010	Canadian Navy, Gold plated (Cr)	10.00	2013	Blue-Winged Teal (SP)	12.00
2010	Sask. Roughriders, Gold plated (Cr)	10.00	2014	Ferruginous Hawk (SP)	12.00
2011	Great Grey Owl (SP)	10.00	2015	Blue Jay (SP)	12.00

Note: The nickel-bronze collector dollars of 2010-2015 were issued singly or in Specimen or Proof sets.

NICKEL DOLLARS

2007-2008 NHL HOCKEY SEASON (Gift Sets)

Calgary Flames

Edmonton Oilers

Montreal Canadiens

Ottawa Senators

Toronto Maple Leafs

Vancouver Canucks

Date	Description	Buying Price	Date	Description	Buying Price
2008	Calgary Flames	10.00	2008	Ottawa Sentaors	10.00
2008	Edmonton Oilers	10.00	2008	Toronto Maple Leafs	10.00
2008	Montreal Canadiens	10.00	2008	Vancouver Canucks	10.00

2007-2008 NHL HOCKEY SEASON (Pucks)

Calgary Flames

Edmonton Oilers

Montreal Canadiens

Ottawa Senators

Toronto Maple Leafs

Vancouver Canucks

Date	Description	Buying Price	Date	Description	Buying Price
2008	Calgary Flames	10.00	2008	Ottawa Senators	10.00
2008	Edmonton Oilers	10.00	2008	Toronto Maple Leafs	10.00
2008	Montreal Canadiens	10.00	2008	Vancouver Canucks	10.00

NICKEL DOLLARS

2008-2009 NHL HOCKEY SEASON (Key Chains)

Calgary Flames

Edmonton Oilers

Montreal Canadiens

Ottawa Senators

Toronto Maple Leafs

Vancouver Canucks

Date	Description	Buying Price	Date	Description	Buying Price
2009	Calgary Flames	10.00	2009	Ottawa Sentaors	10.00
2009	Edmonton Oilers	10.00	2009	Toronto Maple Leafs	10.00
2009	Montreal Canadiens	10.00	2009	Vancouver Canucks	10.00

2008-2009 NHL HOCKEY SEASON (Gift Sets)

Calgary Flames

Edmonton Oilers

Montreal Canadiens

Ottawa Senators

Toronto Maple Leafs

Vancouver Canucks

Date	Description	Buying Price	Date	Description	Buying Price
2009	Calgary Flames	10.00	2009	Ottawa Senators	10.00
2009	Edmonton Oilers	10.00	2009	Toronto Maple Leafs	10.00
2009	Montreal Canadiens	10.00	2009	Vancouver Canucks	10.00

THREE-PLY BRASS PLATED STEEL DOLLARS

OCCASIONS, 2014

OCCASIONS 2015

Stork
Baby Set

Gifts and Ballons
Birthday Set

Teddy Bear
Baby Set

Three Ballons
Birthday Set

Maple Leaf
O Canada Set

Two Turtle Dove
Wedding Set

Large Maple Leaf
O Canada Set

Two Swans
Wedding Set

Date	Description	Buying Price
2015	Teddy Bear, Baby Set	10.00
2015	Three Balloons, Birthday Set	10.00
2015	Large Maple Leaf, O Canada Set	10.00
2015	Two Swan, Wedding Set	10.00

Reindeer
Holiday Set

Date	Description	Buying Price
2014	Stork, Baby Set	10.00
2014	Gifts and Balloons, Birthday Set	10.00
2014	Maple Leaf, O Canada Set	10.00
2014	Two Turtle Doves, Wedding Set	10.00
2014	Reindeer, Holiday Set	10.00

2 DOLLAR COINS

1996 Polar Bear

1999 Nunavut Mule

ELIZABETH II 1996

Date	Description	Buying Price
1996	Specimen, Nickel/bronze	5.00
1996	Proof, Nickel/bronze	5.00
1996	Proof, Silver/gilt	10.00
1996	Piedfort, Silver/gilt	50.00
1996	Gold/gold	245.00

Date	Description	Buying Price
1999	Mule, No Ring	100.00

2000 Path of Knowledge (Gold)

ELIZABETH II 2000

Date	Description	Buying Price
2000	BU, Nickel/bronze	5.00
2000	Specimen, Nickel/bronze	5.00
2000	Proof, Silver/gilt	10.00
2000	Proof, Gold/gold	245.00

1999 Nunavut - Reverse Ring

1999 Nunavut Gold - No Reverse Ring

ELIZABETH II 1999

Date	Description	Buying Price
1999	Specimen, Nickel/bronze	5.00
1999	Proof, Silver/gilt	15.00
1999	Proof, Gold/gold	245.00

ELIZABETH II 2000-2001

Date	Description	Buying Price
2000	Specimen, Nickel/bronze	5.00
2001	Specimen, Nickel/bronze	5.00

2 DOLLAR COINS

2004 Polar Bear

ELIZABETH II 2004

Date	Description	Buying Price
2004	Proof, Silver	20.00

10th Anniversary

ELIZABETH II 2006

Date	Description	Buying Price
2006	Proof, Gold/gold	400.00

Churchill Reverse

ELIZABETH II 2006

Date	Description	Buying Price
2006	BU, Nickel/bronze	5.00

YOUNG WILDLIFE SERIES
Specimen, Nickel/bronze

2010 Lynx Kittens   2011 Elk Calf

2012 Wolf Cubs   2013 Black Bears Cubs

2014 Baby Rabbits   2015 Racoons

ELIZABETH II 2010-2014

Date	Description	Buying Price
2010	Lynx Kittens	15.00
2011	Elk Calf	15.00
2012	Wolf Cubs	15.00
2013	Black Bears	15.00
2014	Baby Rabbits Cubs	15.00
2015	Racoons	15.00

3 DOLLAR COMMEMORATIVES

2006 The Beaver

2010 Return of the Tyee

2011 Family Scene

Date	Description	Buying Price	Date	Description	Buying Price
2006	The Beaver	75.00	2011	Family Scene	30.00
2010	Return of the Tyee	30.00			

WILDLIFE CONSERVATION SERIES

2010 Barn Owl

2010 Polar Bear

2011 Orca Whale

2011 Black Footed Ferret

Date	Description	Buying Price	Date	Description	Buying Price
2010	Barn Owl	25.00	2011	Orca Whale	25.00
2010	Polar Bear	25.00	2011	Black Footed Ferret	25.00

BIRTHSTONE SERIES

2011 Obv.

2011 Rev.

2012 Obv.

2012 Rev

Date	Description	Buying Price	Date	Description	Buying Price
2011	January - Garnet	25.00	2012	January - Garnet	25.00
2011	February - Amethyst	25.00	2012	February - Amethyst	25.00
2011	March - Aquamarine	25.00	2012	March - Aquamarine	25.00
2011	April - Diamond	25.00	2012	April - Diamond	25.00
2011	May - Emerald	25.00	2012	May - Emerald	25.00
2011	June - Alexandrite	25.00	2012	June - Alexandrite	25.00
2011	July - Ruby	25.00	2012	July - Ruby	25.00
2011	August - Peridot	25.00	2012	August - Peridot	25.00
2011	September - Sapphire	25.00	2012	September - Sapphire	25.00
2011	October - Tourmaline	25.00	2012	October - Tourmaline	25.00
2011	November - Topaz	25.00	2012	November - Topaz	25.00
2011	December - Zircon	25.00	2012	December - Zircon	25.00

3 DOLLAR COMMEMORATIVES

CANADIAN ANIMAL ARCHITECT SERIES

Bee and Hive

Spider and Web

Caterpilar and Chrysalis

Date	Description	Buying Price
2013	Bee and Hive	30.00
2013	Spider and Web	30.00

Date	Description	Buying Price
2014	Caterpilar and Chrysalis	30.00

THREE DOLLAR COMMEMORATIVES

2013 Hummingbird with Morning Glory

2013 Fishing

2013 Martin Short Presents Canada

2013 Maple Leaf Impression

2013 Life in the North

2014 Jewel of Life

2014 "Wait For Me, Daddy"

2015 50th Anniv. of Canadian Flag

Date	Description	Buying Price
2013	Hummingbird with Morning Glory	30.00
2013	Fishing	20.00
2013	Martin Short Presents Canada	25.00
2013	Maple Leaf Impression	25.00
2013	Life in the North	20.00

Date	Description	Buying Price
2013	Miss Canada: An Allegory	20.00
2014	Jewel of Life	30.00
2014	"Wait For Me, Daddy"	15.00
2015	50th Anniv. Canadian Flag	15.00

4 DOLLAR COMMEMORATIVES

2007 Parasaurolophus

2008 Triceratops

2009 Tyrannosaurus Rex

2010 Dromaeosaurus

2010 Euoplocephalus Tutus

2009 Hanging the Stocking

2011 Welcome to the World

2011 Tecumseh

2011 Sir Isaac Brock

2013 Charles-Michel de Salaberry

2013 Laura Secord

Date	Description	Buying Price
2007	Parasaurolophus	75.00
2008	Triceratops	50.00
2009	Tyrannosaurus Rex	30.00
2010	Dromaeosaurus	30.00
2010	Euoplocephalus Tutus	30.00
2009	Hanging the Stocking	25.00

Date	Description	Buying Price
2011	Welcome to the World	40.00
2012	Tecumseh	25.00
2012	Sir Isaac Brock	25.00
2013	Charles-Michel de Salaberry	25.00
2013	Laura Secord	25.00

5 DOLLAR SILVER COMMEMORATIVES

50TH ANNIVERSARY OF BETHUNE'S ARRIVAL IN CHINA

Canada $5

China

VIKING SETTLEMENT

Canada $5

Norway 20 Kroner

100TH ANNIVERSARY OF MARCONI'S FIRST MESSAGE ACROSS THE ATLANTIC

Canada $5

British £2

2006 WORLD CUP OF SOCCER, GERMANY

Date	Description	Buying Price
1998	Bethune, 2-coin set	45.00
1999	Viking Settlement, 2-coin set	25.00

Date	Description	Buying Price
2001	Marconi, 2- coin set	20.00
2003	2006 World Cup of Soccer	25.00

5 DOLLAR SILVER COMMEMORATIVES

Common obv. 2004-2005

2004 100th Anniversary
Canadian Open Championship

2004 Majestic Moose

2005 60th Anniversary of the end
of the Second World War

Common obv. 2005-2006

2005 White-tailed Deer and Fawn

2005 Atlantic Walrus and Calf

2006 Peregrine Falcon
and Nestlings

2006 Sable Island Horse
and Foal

Date	Description	Buying Price	Date	Description	Buying Price
2004	100th Anniv. Canadian Open Golf	20.00	2005	White-tailed Deer and Fawn	30.00
2004	Majestic Moose	75.00	2005	Atlantic Walrus and Calf	35.00
2005	60th Anniv. WWII.	20.00	2006	Peregrine Falcon and Nestlings	35.00
2005	60th Anniv. WWII, ML Privy Mark	50.00	2006	Sable Island Horse and Foal	35.00

5 DOLLAR SILVER COMMEMORATIVES

2005 Alberta Centennial

2005 Saskatchewan Centennial

2006 Breast Cancer

2006 Snowbirds

2009 80th Anniversary
of Canada in Japan

2012 25th Anniv. of the Rick
Hansen Man-in-Motion Tour

2012 Georgina Pope

2013 Royal Infant Toys

2013 Devil's Brigade

Date	Description	Buying Price	Date	Description	Buying Price
2005	Alberta Centennial	25.00	2012	Rick Hansen	25.00
2005	Saskatchewan Centennial	25.00	2012	Georgina Pope	30.00
2006	Breast Cancer	30.00	2013	Royal Infant Toys	35.00
2006	Snowbirds	20.00	2013	Devil's Brigade	30.00
2009	80th Anniv. Canada in Japan	30.00			

5 DOLLAR SILVER COMMEMORATIVES

2011 Full Buck Moon

2011 Full Hunter's Moon

2012 Full Wolf Moon

2012 Full Pink Moon

2013 Mother and Baby Ice Fishing

2013 Ice Fishing Father

2013 Tradition of Hunting Deer

2013 Tradition of Hunting Bison

2013 Seascape Theme Vignette

2014 Hunting in Harmony

2014 St. George Slaying Dragon

2014 Alice Munro

Date	Description	Buying Price	Date	Description	Buying Price
2011	Full Buck Moon	60.00	2013	Hunting Deer	30.00
2011	Full Hunter's Moon	60.00	2013	Hunting Bison	30.00
2012	Full Wolf Moon	60.00	2013	Seascape Theme Vignette	30.00
2012	Full Pink Moon	60.00	2014	Hunting in Harmony	30.00
2013	Mother and Baby Ice Fishing	60.00	2014	St. George Slaying the Dragon	30.00
2013	Ice Fishing Father	60.00	2014	Allice Munro	30.00

5 DOLLAR SILVER COMMEMORATIVES

2014 Poinsettia

2014 Rose

2014 Tulip

2014 Canadian Expeditionary Force

2014 Lion on Mountain Vignette

2014 Princess to Monarch

2015 Canada Goose

2015 Canadian Banknote Vignette

2015 Year of the Sheep

Date	Description	Buying Price	Date	Description	Buying Price
2014	Poinsettia	60.00	2014	Princess to Monarch	30.00
2014	Rose	60.00	2015	Canada Goose	30.00
2014	Tulip	60.00	2015	Canadian Banknote Vignette	35.00
2014	Can. Expeditionary Force	30.00	2015	Year of the Sheep	35.00
2014	Lion on Mountain Vignette	35.00			

5 AND 10 DOLLAR SILVER COMMEMORATIVES
MONTREAL 1976 OLYMPIC GAMES

For the Summer Olympic Games of 1976, held in Montreal, seven series of silver coins were minted. There were four different coins in each series. Two $5.00 and two $10.00 coins, struck in sterling silver. The $5.00 coins weigh 24.3 grams and the $10.00 coins weigh 48.6 grams. The coins were available, encapsulated in plastic, as single coins, and in custom, prestige and proof four-coin sets. Each set of four coins, with a face value of $30.00, contains 4.28 oz. of fine silver. The purchase price of these sets is linked to the market price of silver, even if the intrinsic value falls below the face value. Large quantities of these coins were issued, and they are not redeemable by the government or the banks.

SERIES I

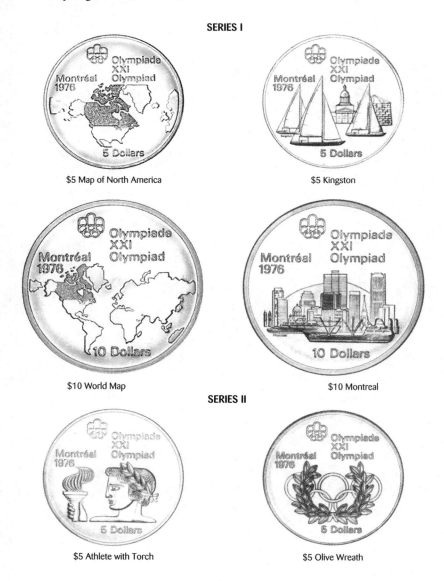

$5 Map of North America

$5 Kingston

$10 World Map

$10 Montreal

SERIES II

$5 Athlete with Torch

$5 Olive Wreath

5 AND 10 DOLLAR SILVER COMMEMORATIVES

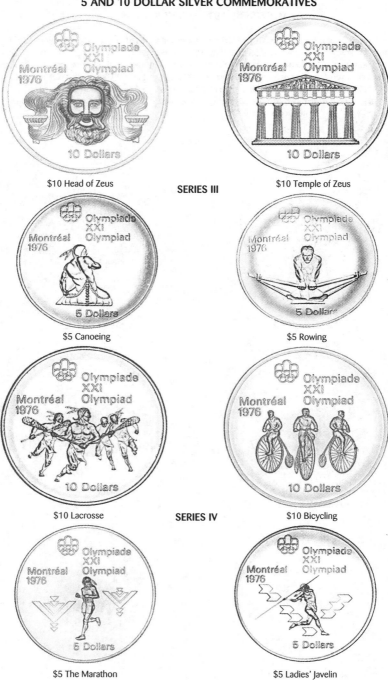

$10 Head of Zeus   SERIES III $10 Temple of Zeus

$5 Canoeing $5 Rowing

$10 Lacrosse   SERIES IV $10 Bicycling

$5 The Marathon $5 Ladies' Javelin

5 AND 10 DOLLAR SILVER COMMEMORATIVES

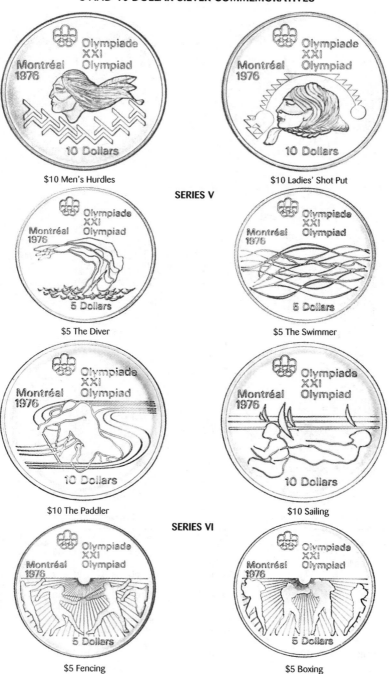

$10 Men's Hurdles $10 Ladies' Shot Put

SERIES V

$5 The Diver $5 The Swimmer

$10 The Paddler $10 Sailing

SERIES VI

$5 Fencing $5 Boxing

5 AND 10 DOLLAR SILVER COMMEMORATIVES

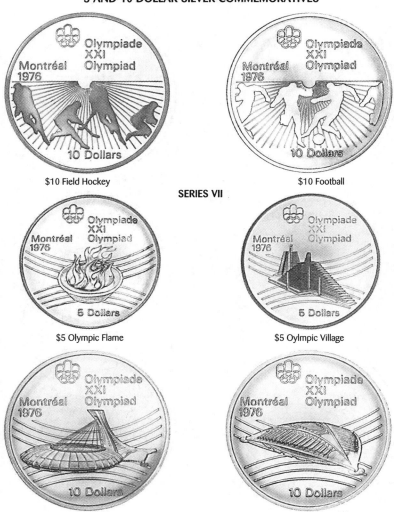

$10 Field Hockey

SERIES VII

$10 Football

$5 Olympic Flame

$5 Oylmpic Village

$10 Olympic Stadium

$10 Olympic Velodrome

Date	Series	$5 Coin	$10 Coin	Custom Set	Prestige Set	Proof Set
1973	1	11.00	22.00	66.00	66.00	66.00
1974	Mule	–	150.00	–	–	–
1974	2	11.00	22.00	66.00	66.00	66.00
1974	3	11.00	22.00	66.00	66.00	66.00
1975	4	11.00	22.00	66.00	66.00	66.00
1975	5	11.00	22.00	66.00	66.00	66.00
1976	6	11.00	22.00	66.00	66.00	66.00
1976	7	11.00	22.00	66.00	66.00	66.00

Note: A set equals 2 x $5.00 coins and 2 x $10.00 coins of the same year.

8 DOLLAR SILVER COMMEMORATIVES

2004 Great Grizzly

2005 Railway Bridge

2005 Chinese Memorial

2007 Trade in Ancient China Obv.

2007 Trade in Ancient China Rev.

2007 Maple of Long Life

2009 Maple of Wisdom

2010 Maple of Strength

Date	Description	Buying Price
2004	Great Grizzly	35.00
2005	Railway Bridge	30.00
2005	Chinese Memorial	30.00
2007	Trade in Ancient China	30.00

Date	Description	Buying Price
2007	Maple of Long Life	30.00
2009	Maple of Wisdom	60.00
2010	Maple of Strength	60.00

10 DOLLAR SILVER COMMEMORATIVES

2005 Year of the Veteran

2005 Pope John Paul II

2006 Fortress of Louisbourg

2010 Blue Whale

2010 75th Anniv. First Bank Notes Issued by the Bank of Canada

2011 Highway of Heroes

2011 Boreal Forest

2011 Orca Whale

2011 Peregrine Falcon

Date	Description	Buying Price	Date	Description	Buying Price
2005	Year of the Veteran	25.00	2011	Highway of Heroes	30.00
2005	Pope John Paul II	25.00	2011	Boreal Forest	35.00
2006	Fortress of Louisbourg	25.00	2011	Orca Whale	35.00
2010	Blue Whale	35.00	2011	Peregrine Falcon	35.00
2010	75th Anniv. Bank of Canada	25.00			

10 DOLLAR SILVER COMMEMORATIVES

2011 Wood Bison

2011 Winter Town

2011 Little Skaters

2012 Year of the Dragon

2012 RMS Titanic

2012 HMS Shannon

2012 Praying Mantis

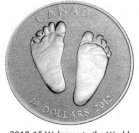
2012-15 Welcome to the World

2013 Year of the Snake

2013 Year of the Snake

2013 Winter Scene

2013 Dreamcatcher

Date	Description	Buying Price	Date	Description	Buying Price
2011	Wood Bison	35.00	2012	Welcome to the World	40.00
2011	Winter Town	30.00	2013	Welcome to the World	30.00
2011	Little Skaters	30.00	2013	Year of the Snake	20.00
2012	Year of the Dragon	20.00	2013	Year / Snake (Chineses Character)	20.00
2012	RMS Titanic	40.00	2013	Winter Scene	35.00
2012	HMS Shannon	35.00	2013	Dreamcatcher	35.00
2012	Praying Mantis				

10 DOLLAR SILVER COMMEMORATIVES - "O CANADA SERIES"

The Inukshuk	The Beaver	The RCMP
The Polar Bear	Summer Fun	The Wolf
Niagara Falls	The Caribou	Hockey
The Orca	Maple Leaf (with colour)	Canadian Holiday Season

Date	Description	Buying Price	Date	Description	Buying Price
2013	The Inukshuk	20.00	2013	Niagara Falls	20.00
2013	The Beaver	20.00	2013	The Caribou	20.00
2013	The RCMP	20.00	2013	Hockey	20.00
2013	The Polar Bear	20.00	2013	The Orca	20.00
2013	Summer Fun	20.00	2013	Maple Leaf (with colour)	20.00
2013	The Wolf	20.00	2013	Canadian Holiday Season	20.00

10 DOLLAR SILVER COMMEMORATIVES

2013 Mallard

2013 Wood Duck

2013 Maple Leaf

2013 Skimmer Dragonfly

2013 Superman™: Vintage

2013 Partridge in Pear Tree

2013 Holiday Candles

2014 Northen Pintail

2014 Harlequin Duck

2014 Year of the Horse

2014 Maple Leaf

2014 Green Darner Dragonfly

Date	Description	Buying Price	Date	Description	Buying Price
2013	Mallard	35.00	2013	Holiday Candles	35.00
2013	Wood Duck	35.00	2014	Northern Pintail	35.00
2013	Maple Leaf	20.00	2014	Harlequin Duck	35.00
2013	12-Spotted Skimmer Dragonfly	40.00	2014	Year of the Horse	20.00
2013	Superman™: Vintage	25.00	2014	Maple Leaf	20.00
2013	Partridge in a Pear Tree	30.00	2014	Green Darner Dragonfly	40.00

10 DOLLAR SILVER COMMEMORATIVES

2014 FIFA™ World Cup

2014 Skating in Canada

2014 Mobilisation of our Nation

2014 Pope John Paul II

2014 70th Anniv. of D-Day

2014 "Wait For Me, Daddy"

2014 Superman Cover #1 (1938)

2015 Cinnamon Teal

2015 Pygmy Snaketail

2015 Maple Leaf

2015 Year of the Sheep

2015 Celebrating Canada

Date	Description	Buying Price	Date	Description	Buying Price
2014	Welcome to the World	30.00	2014	Superman Cover #1 (1938)	30.00
2014	FIFA™ World Cup	25.00	2015	Cinnamon Teal	35.00
2014	Skating in Canada	30.00	2015	Pygmy Snaketail	35.00
2014	Mobilisation of our Nation	30.00	2015	Maple Leaf	15.00
2014	Pope John Paul II	30.00	2015	Year of the Sheep	20.00
2014	70th Anniv. D-Day	30.00	2015	Celebrating Canada	30.00
2014	"Wait For Me, Daddy"	30.00			

15 DOLLAR SILVER COMMEMORATIVES
OLYMPIC CENTENNIAL COINS

100th Anniv. of Olympic Movement
Speed Skater, Pole Vaulter,
Gymnast

100th Anniv. of Olympic Movement
The Spirit of the Generations

Date	Description	Buying Price	Date	Description	Buying Price
1992	Speed Skater, Pole Vaulter, Gymnast	25.00	1992	The Spirit of the Generations	25.00

CHINESE LUNAR CALENDAR SILVER COMMEMORATIVES

1998 Year of the Tiger   1999 Year of the Rabbit   2000 Year of the Dragon

2001 Year of the Snake   2002 Year of the Horse   2003 Year of the Ram

CHINESE LUNAR CALENDAR SILVER COMMEMORATIVES (cont.)

2004 Year of the Monkey   2005 Year of the Rooster   2006 Year of the Dog

2007 Year of the Pig   2008 Year of the Rat   2009 Year of the Ox

Date	Description	Buying Price	Date	Description	Buying Price
1998	Tiger	125.00	2004	Monkey	50.00
1999	Rabbit	40.00	2005	Rooster	40.00
2000	Dragon	55.00	2006	Dog	50.00
2001	Snake	30.00	2007	Pig	50.00
2002	Horse	35.00	2008	Rat	50.00
2003	Ram	35.00	2009	Ox	50.00

15 DOLLAR SILVER COMMEMORATIVES

VIGNETTES OF ROYALTY SERIES

Commonn Obverse

2008 Victoria

2008 Edward VII

2008 George V

2009 George VI

2009 Elizabeth II

Date	Description	Buying Price	Date	Description	Buying Price
2008	Victoria	60.00	2009	George VI	60.00
2008	Edward VII	60.00	2009	Ellizabeth II	60.00
2008	George V	60.00			

PLAYING CARD MONEY SERIES

2008 Jack of Hearts

2008 Queen of Spades

2009 King of Hearts

2009 Ten of Spades

Date	Description	Buying Price	Date	Description	Buying Price
2008	Jack of Hearts	50.00	2009	King of Hearts	50.00
2008	Queen of Spades	50.00	2009	Ten of Spades	50.00

15 DOLLAR SILVER COMMEMORATIVES

LUNAR LOTUS SERIES

2010 Year of the Tiger

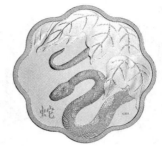

2013 Year of the Snake

2011 Year of the Rabbit

2014 Year of the Horse

2012 Year of the Dragon

2015 Year of the Sheep

Date	Description	Buying Price	Date	Description	Buying Price
2010	Year of the Tiger	70.00	2013	Year of the Snake	55.00
2011	Year of the Rabbit	65.00	2014	Year of the Horse	50.00
2012	Year of the Dragon	55.00	2015	Year of the Sheep	50.00

CLASSIC CHINESE ZODIAC SERIES

2010 Year of the Tiger

2013 Year of the Snake

2011 Year of the Rabbit

2014 Year of the Horse

2012 Year of the Dragon

2015 Year of the Sheep

Date	Description	Buying Price	Date	Description	Buying Price
2010	Year of the Tiger	85.00	2013	Year of the Snake	55.00
2011	Year of the Rabbit	115.00	2014	Year of the Horse	50.00
2012	Year of the Dragon	55.00	2015	Year of the Sheep	50.00

15 DOLLAR SILVER COMMEMORATIVES

2011 Prince William

2011 Prince Harry

2011 The Prince of Wales

2011 Maple of Happiness

2012 Maple of Good Fortune

2013 Maple of Peace

2013 Superman™: Modern Day

2014 Maple of Longevity

2014 Superman™
Action Comics # 419

Date	Description	Buying Price	Date	Description	Buying Price
2011	Prince William	50.00	2013	Maple of Peace	55.00
2011	Prince Harry	50.00	2013	Superman™: Modern Day	55.00
2011	The Prince of Wales	50.00	2014	Maple of Longevity	50.00
2011	Maple of Happiness	55.00	2014	Superman™ Action Comics #419	50.00
2012	Maple of Good Fortune	55.00			

20 DOLLAR SILVER COMMEMORATIVES
Calgary 1988 Olympic Winter Games

Downhill Skiing

Speed Skating

Hockey

Biathalon

Cross-Country Skiing

Free-Style Skiing

Figure Skating

Curling

Ski Jumping

Bobsleigh

Date	Description	Buying Price
1985	Downhill Skiiing	20.00
1985	Speed Skating	20.00
1985	Speed Skating, no edge lettering	100.00
1986	Hockey	20.00
1986	Hockey, no edge lettering	100.00
1986	Biathalon	20.00
1986	Biathalon, no edge lettering	100.00
1986	Cross-Country Skiing	20.00
1986	Free-Style Skiing	20.00
1986	Free-Style Skiing, no edge lettering	100.00
1987	Figure Skating	20.00
1987	Curling	20.00
1987	Ski Jumping	20.00
1987	Bobsleigh	20.00

20 DOLLAR SILVER COMMEMORATIVES
Aviation Series One, 1990 - 1994

Anson and Harvard /Robert Leckie

Avro Lancaster /J. E. Fauquier

A. E. A. Silver Dart / F. W. Baldwin and J. A. D. McCurdy

de Havilland Beaver / Phillip C. Garratt

Curtiss JN-4 (Canuck) / Sir F. W. Baillie

de Havilland Gypsy Moth / Murton A. Seymour

Fairchild 71C / J. A. Richardson

Super Electra / Z. L. Leigh

Curtiss HS-2L / Stuart Graham

Coin No. 10
Vickers Vedette / T. Reid

Date	Description	Buying Price
1990	Anson and Harvard / Leckie	30.00
1990	Lancaster / Fauquier	65.00
1991	Silver Dart / Baldwin, McCurdy	30.00
1991	Beaver / Garratt	30.00
1992	Curtiss / Baille	30.00
1992	Gypsy Moth / Seymour	30.00
1993	Fairchild / Richardson	30.00
1993	Super Electra / Leigh	30.00
1994	Curtiss / Graham	30.00
1994	Vedette / Reid	30.00

20 DOLLAR SILVER COMMEMORATIVES
Aviation Series Two 1995 - 1999

The Fleet 80 Canuck / Noury

DHC-1 Chipmunk / Bannock

CF-100 Canuck / Zurakowski

CF-105 Arrow / Chamberlain

Canadian F-86 Sabre /
Fern Villeneuve

Canadair CT-114 Tutor /
Edward Higgins

CP-107 Argus /
William S. Longhurst

CL-215 Waterbomber /
Paul Gagnon

DHC-6 Twin Otter / G. A. Neal

DHC-8 Dash 8 / R. H. Fowler

Date	Description	Buying Price
1995	Fleet 80 Canuck / Noury	30.00
1995	DHC-1 Chipmunk / Bannock	50.00
1996	CF-100 Canuck / Zurakowski	30.00
1996	CF-105 Arrow / Chamberlin	75.00
1997	F-86 Sabre / Villeneuve	30.00
1997	CT-114 Tutor / Higgin	30.00
1998	CP-107 Argus / Longhurst	30.00
1998	CL-215 Waterbomber / Gagnon	50.00
1999	DHC-6 Twin Otter / Neal	50.00
1999	DHC-8 Dash 8 / Fowler	30.00

20 DOLLAR SILVER COMMEMORATIVES

LAND, SEA AND RAIL 2000 - 2002

Coin No. 1 H. S. Taylor Steam Buggy	Coin No. 2 The Bluenose	Coin No. 3 The Toronto
Coin No. 4 The Russel "Light Four"	Coin No. 5 The Marco Polo	Coin No. 6 The Scotia
Coin No. 7 The Gray-Dort	Coin No. 8 The William Lawrence	Coin No. 9 D-10 Locomotive

Date	Coin No.	Description	Buying Price
2000	1	H. S. Taylor Steam Buggy	30.00
2000	2	The Bluenose	85.00
2000	3	The Toronto	30.00
2001	4	The Russel "Light Four"	30.00
2001	5	The Marco Polo	30.00
2001	6	The Scotia	30.00
2002	7	The Gray-Dort	30.00
2002	8	The William Lawrence	30.00
2002	9	The D-10 Locomotive	30.00

20 DOLLAR SILVER COMMEMORATIVES

LAND, SEA AND RAIL 2003

Coin No. 10
HMCS Bras d'Or

Coin No. 11
CNR FA-1 Diesel Electric

Coin No. 12
Bricklin SV-1

Date	Coin No.	Description	Buying Price
2003	10	HMCS Bras d'Or	30.00
2003	11	C.N.R. FA-1 Diesel Electric Locomotive - No. 9400	30.00
2003	12	Bricklin SV-1	35.00

NATURAL WONDERS COLLECTION

Coin No. 1 Niagara Falls

Coin No. 2 Rocky Mountains

Coin No. 3 Icebergs

Coin No. 4 Northern Lights

Coin No. 5 Hopewell Rocks

Coin No. 6 Diamonds

Date	Coin No.	Description	Buying Price
2003	1	Niagara Falls	40.00
2003	2	Rocky Mountains	30.00
2004	3	Icebergs	30.00
2004	4	Northern Lights	35.00
2004	5	Hopewell Rocks	30.00
2005	6	Diamonds	30.00

20 DOLLAR SILVER COMMEMORATIVES

TALL SHIPS COLLECTION

Coin No. 1 Three-Masted Ship   Coin No. 2 Ketch   Coin No. 3 Brigantine

Date	Coin No.	Description	Buying Price
2005	1	Three-masted Ship, Hologram	35.00
2006	2	Ketch, Hologram	45.00
2007	3	Brigantine, Hologram	45.00

NATIONAL PARKS SERIES

Coin No. 1
North Pacific
Rim

Coin No. 2
Mingan
Archipelago

Coin No. 3 Georgian Bay Islands   Coin No. 4 Nahanni National Park   Coin No. 5 Jasper National Park

Date	Coin No.	Description	Buying Price
2005	1	North Pacific Rim National Park Reserve	35.00
2005	2	Mingan Archipelago National Park Reserve	35.00
2006	3	Georgian Bay Islands National Park	35.00
2006	4	Nahanni National Park Reserve	40.00
2006	5	Jasper National Park	40.00

20 DOLLAR SILVER COMMEMORATIVES

CANADIAN ARCHITECTURAL COLLECTION

Coin No. 1 Notre Dame Basilica	Coin No. 2 CN Tower	Coin No. 3 Pengrowth Saddledome

Date	Coin No.	Description	Buying Price
2006	1	Notre Dame Basilica, Hologram	40.00
2006	2	30th Anniversary CN Tower, Hologram	40.00
2006	3	Pengrowth Saddledome, Hologram	40.00

HOLIDAY SERIES

2007 Holiday Sleigh Ride

2008 Holiday Carols

2010 Holiday Pine Cones

2011 Christmas Tree

Date	Description	Buying Price
2007	Holiday Sleigh Ride	50.00
2008	Holiday Carols	30.00
2010	Holiday Pine Cones, Moonlight	50.00
2010	Holiday Pine Cones, Ruby	50.00
2011	Christmas Tree	55.00

20 DOLLAR SILVER COMMEMORATIVES

CRYSTAL SNOWFLAKES

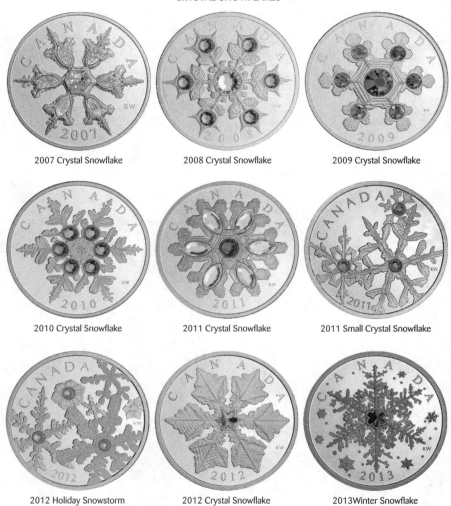

2007 Crystal Snowflake   2008 Crystal Snowflake   2009 Crystal Snowflake

2010 Crystal Snowflake   2011 Crystal Snowflake   2011 Small Crystal Snowflake

2012 Holiday Snowstorm   2012 Crystal Snowflake   2013 Winter Snowflake

Date	Description	Buying Price	Date	Description	Buying Price
2007	Crystal Snowflake, Aquamarine	225.00	2011	Crystal Snowflake, Emerald	50.00
2007	Crystal Snowflake, Irridescent	250.00	2011	Crystal Snowflake, Topaz	50.00
2008	Crystal Snowflake, Amethyst	80.00	2011	Crystal Snowflake, Hyacinth	50.00
2008	Crystal Snowflake, Sapphire	80.00	2011	Crystal Snowflake, Montana	50.00
2009	Crystal Snowflake, Blue	70.00	2012	Holiday Snowstorm	60.00
2009	Crystal Snowflake, Rose	75.00	2012	Crystal Snowflake	60.00
2010	Crystal Snowflake, Blue	50.00	2013	Winter Snowflake	60.00
2010	Crystal Snowflake, Tanzanite	50.00			

20 DOLLAR SILVER COMMEMORATIVES

2007 125th Anniv. First
Int'l Polar Year, Silver

2007 125th Anniv. First
Int'l Polar Year, Blue Plasma

2008 AgricultureTrade

2008 Crystal Raindrop

2008 The Royal Hudson

2009 Autumn Crystal Raindrop

2009 Coal Mining Trade

2009 The Jubilee

2009 Summer Moon Mask

Date	Description	Buying Price
2007	Int'l Polar Year, Silver	40.00
2007	Int'l Polar Year, Blue Plasma	100.00
2008	Agriculture Trade	35.00
2008	Crystal Raindrop	85.00
2008	The Royal Hudson	50.00

Date	Description	Buying Price
2009	Autumn Crystal Raindrop	100.00
2009	Coal Mining Trade	40.00
2009	The Jubilee	45.00
2009	Summer Moon Mask	100.00

20 DOLLAR SILVER COMMEMORATIVES

2009 Calgary Flames

2009 Edmonton Oilers

2009 Montreal Canadiens

2009 Ottawa Senators

2009 Toronto Maple Leafs

2009 Vancouver Canucks

2009 475th Anniv. Jacques Cartier
Arriving at Gaspe

2010 75th Anniv. of the First
Notes Issued by Bank of Canada

2010 Maple Leaf Crystal Raindrop

Date	Description	Buying Price	Date	Description	Buying Price
2009	Calgary Flames	40.00	2009	Vancouver Canucks	40.00
2009	Edmonton Oilers	40.00	2009	475th Anniv. Jacques Cartier's	
2009	Montreal Canadiens	40.00		Arrival at Gaspe	150.00
2009	Ottawa Senators	40.00	2010	First Bank Notes/Bank of Canada	40.00
2009	Toronto Maple Leafs	40.00	2010	Maple Leaf with Crystal Raindrop	60.00

20 DOLLAR SILVER COMMEMORATIVES

2010 The Selkirk

2010 Water Lily

2011 Crystal Dewdrop & Wild Rose

2011 Crystal Raindrop & Maple Leaf

2011 D-10

2011 HRH Prince William of Wales
and Miss Catherine Middleton

2011 Tulip with Ladybug

2011 Winter Scene

2012 Aster with Bumble Bee

Date	Description	Buying Price	Date	Description	Buying Price
2010	The Selkirk	45.00	2011	Prince William/Catherine Middleton	50.00
2010	Water Lily	60.00	2011	Tulip with Ladybug	400.00
2011	Crystal Dewdrop and Wild Rose	60.00	2011	Winter Scene	45.00
2011	Crystal Raindrop and Maple Leaf	60.00	2012	Aster with Bumble Bee	125.00
2011	D-10	45.00			

20 DOLLAR SILVER COMMEMORATIVES

2012 The Bull Moose

2012 Fifty Years of the
Canadian Coast Guard

2012 Houses, Cobalt (1931-1932)
Franklin Carmichael

2012 Nova Scotia Fishing Village
Arthur Lismer

2012 Queen Elizabeth II and
Prince Philip

2012 The Queen's Diamond Jubilee

2012 The Queen's Portrait

2021 The Queen's Visit to Canada

2012 Rhododendron

Date	Description	Buying Price		Date	Description	Buying Price
2012	The Bull Moose	65.00		2012	Queen's Diamond Jubilee	55.00
2012	Canadian Coast Guard	65.00		2012	Queen's Portrait	60.00
2012	Houses, Colbalt (1931-1932)	50.00		2012	Queen's Visit to Canada	40.00
2012	Nova Scotia Fishing Village	55.00		2012	Rhododendron	65.00
2012	Queen Elizabeth II /Prince Philip	40.00				

20 DOLLAR SILVER COMMEMORATIVES

2012 Royal Cypher
60th Jubilee

2012 Stormy Weather, Georgian Bay
F. H. Varley

2012 The Sugar Maple

2012 The Three Wise Men

2012 Winnipeg Jets

2013 Arctic Fox

2013 Autumn Bliss

2013 Bathygnathus Borealis

2013 Beaver

Date	Description	Buying Price	Date	Description	Buying Price
2012	Royal Cypher, 60th Jubilee	40.00	2013	Arctic Fox	45.00
2012	Stormy Weather, Georgian Bay	50.00	2013	Autumn Bliss	65.00
2012	Sugar Maple	60.00	2013	Bathygnathus Borealis	45.00
2012	Three Wise Men	60.00	2013	Beaver	50.00
2012	Winnipeg Jets	50.00			

20 DOLLAR SILVER COMMEMORATIVES

2013 Birth of Royal Infant
"Baby Bears"

2013 Birth of Royal Infant
"Baby Crib"

2013 Birth of Royal Infant
"Hands"

2013 Blue Flag Iris

2013 Canadian Contemporary Art

2013 Canadian Tiger Swallowtail

2013 Canadian Maple Canopy
" Autumn"

2013 Canadian Maple Canopy
"Spring"

2013 Candy Cane

Date	Description	Buying Price	Date	Description	Buying Price
2013	Birth or Royal Infant, "Baby Bears"	40.00	2013	Canadian Tiger Swallowtail	50.00
2013	Birth or Royal Infant, "Baby Crib"	40.00	2013	Canadian Maple Canopy "Autumn"	50.00
2013	Birth or Royal Infant, "Hands"	40.00	2013	Canadian Maple Canopy "Spring"	50.00
2013	Blue Flag Iris	65.00	2013	Candy Cane	80.00
2013	Canadian Contemporary Art	45.00			

20 DOLLAR SILVER COMMEMORATIVES

2013 The Fielder (Baseball)

2013 The Great Hare

2013 The Guardian of the Gorge

2013 The Hitter (Baseball)

2013 Holiday Wreath

2013 Lifelong Mates

2013 Maple Leaf Impression (red)

2013 Mother Protecting Her Eaglets

2013 The Pitcher (Baseball)

Date	Description	Buying Price	Date	Description	Buying Price
2013	The Fielder (Baseball)	55.00	2013	Lifelong Mates	60.00
2013	The Great Hare	50.00	2013	Maple Leaf Impression (red)	55.00
2013	Guardian of the Gorge, F. Johnston	50.00	2013	Mother Protecting Her Eaglets	60.00
2013	The Hitter (Baseball)	55.00	2013	The Pitcher (Baseball)	55.00
2013	Holiday Wreath	60.00			

20 DOLLAR SILVER COMMEMORATIVES

2013 Portrait of Power

2013 Pronghorn

2013 Purple Coneflower
and Eastern Tailed Blue Butterfly

2013 Returning From the Hunt

2013 The Runner (Baseball)

2013 Saint-Tite-des-Caps

2013 Sumacs

2013 Superman™: Man of Steel

2013 Superman™: Metropolis

Date	Description	Buying Price	Date	Description	Buying Price
2013	Portrait of Power	65.00	2013	Saint-Tite-des-Caps, A. Y. Jackson	45.00
2013	Pronghorn	45.00	2013	Sumacs, J. E. H. MacDonald	45.00
2013	Purple Coneflower	40.00	2013	Superman™: Man of Steel	85.00
2013	Returning From The Hunt	55.00	2013	Superman™: Metropolis	90.00
2013	The Runner (Baseball)	60.00			

20 DOLLAR SILVER COMMEMORATIVES

2013 Superman™: The Shield

2013 300th Anniv. of Louisbourg

2013 Toronto Street, Winter Morning
Lawren Harris

2014 25th Anniv. Canadian
Space Agency

2014 75th Anniv. First Royal Visit

2014 75th Anniv. Royal
Winnipeg Ballet

2014 100th Anniv. Hockey Canada

2014 Autumn Falls

2014 Baby Animals: Atlantic Puffin

Date	Description	Buying Price
2013	Superman™: The Shield	90.00
2013	300th Anniv. of Louisbourg	45.00
2013	Toronto Street, Lawren Harris	50.00
2014	25th Anniv. Canadian Space Agency	50.00
2014	75th Anniv. First Royal Visit	50.00

Date	Description	Buying Price
2014	75th Anniv. Royal Winnipeg Ballet	45.00
2014	100th Anniv. Hockey Canada	50.00
2014	Autumn Falls	50.00
2014	Baby Animals: Atlantic Puffin	50.00

20 DOLLAR SILVER COMMEMORATIVES

2014 Baby Animals: Beaver

2014 Bald Eagle with Fish

2014 Canadian Maple Canopy: Autumn Allure

2014 Canadian Maple Canopy: Spring Splendour

2014 Canadian Peacekeeping in Cyprus

2014 Chickadee with Winter Berries

2014 Cougar: Atop a Mountain

2014 Cougar: Perched on Maple Tree

2014 Cougar: Pouncing in the Snow

Date	Description	Buying Price	Date	Description	Buying Price
2014	Baby Animals: Beaver	50.00	2014	Chickadee with Winter Berries	50.00
2014	Bald Eagle with Fish	50.00	2014	Cougar: Atop A Mountain	45.00
2014	Can. Maple Canopy: Autumn Allure	50.00	2014	Cougar: Perched on Maple Tree	50.00
2014	Canadian Maple Canopy: Spring Splendour	50.00	2014	Cougar: Pouncing in the Snow	55.00
2014	Canadian Peacekeeping in Cyprus	55.00			

20 DOLLAR SILVER COMMEMORATIVES

2014 Howling Wolf

2014 Iconic Polar Bear

2014 Iconic Superman™
Annual #1 (2012)

2014 Interconnections:
Air - Thunderbird

2014 Interconnections:
Land - Beaver

2014 Interconnections:
Sea - Orca

2014 Lake Erie

2014 Lake Ontario

2014 Lake Superior

Date	Description	Buying Price	Date	Description	Buying Price
2014	Howling Wolf	55.00	2014	Interconnections: Sea - Orca	50.00
2014	Iconic Polar Bear	50.00	2014	Lake Erie	60.00
2014	Iconic Superman™: Annual #1	50.00	2014	Lake Ontario	55.00
2014	Interconnections: Air - Thunderbird	50.00	2014	Lake Superioir	55.00
2014	Interconnections: Land - Beaver	50.00			

20 DOLLAR SILVER COMMEMORATIVES

2014 Legend of Nanaboozhoo

2014 Majestic Maple Leaves

2014 Majestic Maple Leaves, Coloured

2014 Majestic Maple Leaves with Jade

2014 Maple Leaf Impressio(green)

2014 Nanaboozhoo and the Thunderbird

2014 Nanaboozhoo and the Thunderbird's Nest

2014 Perched Bald Eagle

2014 Pond Hockey

Date	Description	Buying Price	Date	Description	Buying Price
2014	Legend of Nanaboozhoo	50.00	2014	Nanaboozhoo and the Thunderbird	65.00
2014	Majestic Maple Leaves	45.00	2014	Nanaboozhoo & Thunderbird's Nest	45.00
2014	Majestic Maple Leaves, Coloured	50.00	2014	Perched Bald Eagle	55.00
2014	Majestic Maple Leaves with Jade	55.00	2014	Pond Hockey	50.00
2014	Maple Leaf Impression (green)	60.00			

20 DOLLAR SILVER COMMEMORATIVES

2014 Red-Spotted Purple
Butterfly

2014 Red Trillium

2014 River Rapids

2014 RMS Empress of Ireland

2014 Royal Generations

2014 Royal Ontario Museum

2014 Scutellosaurus

2014 Snowman

2014 Soaring Bald Eagle

Date	Description	Buying Price	Date	Description	Buying Price
2014	Red-Spotted Purple Butterfly	50.00	2014	Royal Ontario Museum	60.00
2014	Red Trillium	60.00	2014	Scutellosaurus	45.00
2014	River Rapids	50.00	2014	Snowman	45.00
2014	RMS Empress of Ireland	50.00	2014	Soaring Bald Eagle	50.00
2014	Royal Generations	50.00			

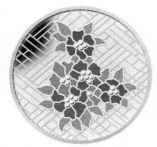

2014 Stained Glass:
Craigdarroch Castle

2014 Stained Glass:
Casa Loma

2014 Totem Forest: Emily Carr

2014 Water-lily and
Leopard Frog

2014 White-tailed Deer:
A Challenge

2014 White-tailed Deer:
A Doe and Her Fawns

2014 White-tailed Deer:
Mates

2014 White-tailed Deer:
Portrait

2014 Wolverine

Date	Description	Buying Price	Date	Description	Buying Price
2014	Stained Glass: Craigdarroch Castle	65.00	2014	White-tailed Deer: A Doe/Her Fawns	50.00
2014	Stained Glass: Casa Loma	65.00	2014	White-tailed Deer: Mates	50.00
2014	Totem Forest, Emily Carr	45.00	2014	White-tailed Deer: Potrait	50.00
2014	Water-lily and Leopard Frog	75.00	2014	Wolverine	45.00
2014	White-tailed Deer: A Challenge	50.00			

2014 Wood Bison:
A Portrait

2014 Wood Bison:
Bull and his Mate

2014 Wood Bison:
Family at Rest

2014 Wood Bison:
The Fight

2014 Woodland Caribou

2014 Xenoceratops
Foremostensis

2015 100th Anniv. of
"In Flanders Fields"

2015 Albertosaurus

2015 Baby Animals:
Black Bear

Date	Description	Buying Price	Date	Description	Buying Price
2014	Wood Bison: A Portrait	50.00	2014	Xenoceratops Foremostensis	45.00
2014	Wood Bison: Bull and His Mate	50.00	2015	100th Anniv. of "In Flanders Fields"	45.00
2014	Wood Bison: Family at Rest	50.00	2015	Albertosaurus	45.00
2014	Wood Bison: The Fight	50.00	2015	Baby Animals: Black Bear	50.00
2014	Woodland Caribou	50.00			

20 DOLLAR SILVER COMMEMORATIVES

2015 Baby Animals:
Burrowing Owl

2015 Battle For Britain

2015 Beaver at Work

2015 Bighorn Sheep

2015 Carolinian Tulip-tree

2015 George-Étienne Cartier

2015 Ice Dancer

2015 Lake Huron

2015 Lake Michigan

Date	Description	Buying Price	Date	Description	Buying Price
2015	Baby Animals: Burrowing Owl	50.00	2015	George-Étienne Cartier	40.00
2015	Battle For Britain	45.00	2015	Ice Dancer	50.00
2015	Beaver at Work	50.00	2015	Lake Huron	55.00
2015	Bighorn Sheep	50.00	2015	Lake Michigan	55.00
2015	Carolinian Tulip-tree	50.00			

20 DOLLAR SILVER COMMEMORATIVES

2015 Largemouth Bass

2015 Majestic Moose

2015 Northern Pike

2015 Rainbow Trout

2015 Sir John A. Macdonald

2015 Turtle with Broadleaf
Arrowhead Flower

2015 Walleye

2015 Wedding

2015 Wolf

Date	Description	Buying Price	Date	Description	Buying Price
2015	Largemouth Bass	50.00	2015	Turtle / Broadleaf Arrowhead Flower	75.00
2015	Majestic Moose	50.00	2015	Walleye	50.00
2015	Northern Pike	50.00	2015	Wedding	55.00
2015	Rainbow Trout	50.00	2015	Wolf	50.00
2015	Sir John A. Macdonald	45.00			

25 DOLLAR SILVER COMMEMORATIVES

VANCOUVER 2010 OLYMPIC WINTER GAMES

Coin. No. 1
Curling

Coin No. 2
Ice Hockey

Coin No. 3
Athletes' Pride

Coin. No. 4
Biathlon

Coin No. 5
Alpine Skiing

Coin No. 6
Snowboarding

Coin. No. 7
Freestyle Skiing

Coin No. 8
Home of the 2010
Olympic Winter Games

Coin No.
9 Figure Skating

Date	Coin No.	Description	Buying Price
2007	1	Curling	25.00
2007	2	Ice Hockey	25.00
2007	3	Athletes' Pride	25.00
2007	4	Biathlon	25.00
2007	5	Alpine Skiing	25.00
2008	6	Snowboarding	25.00
2008	7	Freestyle Skiing	25.00
2008	8	Home of the 2010 Olympic Winter Games	25.00
2008	9	Figure Skating	25.00

25 DOLLAR SILVER COMMEMORATIVES

VANCOUVER 2010 OLYMPIC WINTER GAMES

| Coin. No. 10 | Coin No. 11 | Coin No. 12 |
| Bobsleigh | Speed Skating | Cross Country Skiing |

| Coin. No. 13 | Coin No. 14 | Coin No. 15 |
| Olympic Spirit | Skeleton | Ski Jumping |

Date	Coin No.	Description	Buying Price
2008	10	Bobsleigh	25.00
2009	11	Speed Skating	25.00
2009	12	Cross Country Skiing	25.00
2009	13	Olympic Spirit	25.00
2009	14	Skeleton	25.00
2009	15	Ski Jumping	25.00

25 DOLLAR SILVER COMMEMORATIVES

Date	Description	Buying Price	Date	Description	Buying Price
2011	Toronto City Map	125.00	2011	Wayne and Walter Gretzky	50.00

O CANADA - SERIES ONE

The Beaver

The Polar Bear

The Wolf

The Caribou

The Orca

Date	Description	Buying Price	Date	Description	Buying Price
2013	The Beaver	45.00	2013	The Caribou	45.00
2013	The Polar Bear	45.00	2013	The Orca	45.00
2013	The Wolf	45.00			

25 DOLLAR SILVER COMMEMORATIVES

75th Anniv. First Royal Visit

Christmas Ornament

The Fierce Canadian Lynx

Date	Description	Buying Price	Date	Description	Buying Price
2014	75th Anniv. First Royal Visit	60.00	2014	The Fierce Canadian Lynx	50.00
2014	Christmas Ornament	60.00			

O CANADA - SERIES TWO

The Igloo

Scenic Skiing in Canada

Under the Maple Tree

Cowboy In Canadian Rockies

Arctic Fox and the Northern Lights

Date	Description	Buying Price	Date	Description	Buying Price
2014	The Igloo	40.00	2014	Cowboy in the Canadian Rockies	40.00
2014	Scenic Skiing in Canada	40.00	2014	Arctic Fox and the Northern Lights	40.00
2014	Under the Maple Tree	40.00			

30 DOLLAR SILVER COMMEMORATIVES

2005 Welcome Figure Totem Pole

2006 5th Anniversary Canadarm

2006 Dog Sled

2006 National War Memorial

2006 Beaumont-Hamel
Newfoundland Memorial

2007 Canadian National
Vimy Memorial

2007 Panoramic Photography
in Canada

2008 IMAX©

2009 International Year
of Astronomy

Date	Description	Buying Price
2005	Welcome Figure Totem Pole	40.00
2006	5th Anniversary Canadarm	45.00
2006	Dog Sled	90.00
2006	National War Memorial	55.00
2006	Beaumont-Hamel Newfoundland Memorial	50.00
2007	Canadian National Vimy Memorial	40.00
2007	Panoramic Photography in Canada	45.00
2008	IMAX©	45.00
2009	International Year of Astronomy	60.00

Note: Illustrations on this page and the Toronto City Map on page 142 are smaller than actual size.

30 DOLLAR SILVER COMMEMORATIVES

Canada Through The
Eyes of Tim Barnard

75th Anniv. of the Declaration
of the Second World War

National Aboriginal Veterans Monument

100th Anniv. of the Completion
of the Grand Trunk ailway

Date	Description	Buying Price
2014	Canada Through the Eyes of Tim Barnard	90.00
2014	75th Anniv. of the Declaration of the Second World War	90.00
2014	National Aboriginal Veterans Monument	90.00
2014	100th Anniv, of the Completion of the Grand Trunk Railway	90.00

Note: Coins illustrated smaller than actual size.

50 DOLLAR SILVER COMMEMORATIVES

2006 The Four Seasons

2009 150th Anniversary of the Start of
Construction of the Parliament Buildings

2007 60th Wedding Anniversary
Queen Elizabeth II and Prince Philip

2010 75th Anniversary of the First Notes
Issued by the Bank of Canada

2008 100th Anniversary of the
Royal Canadian Mint

2012 The Calgary Stampede

Date	Description	Buying Price	Date	Description	Buying Price
2006	The Four Seasons	225.00	2009	Const. of Parliament Buildings	175.00
2007	Queen Elizabeth/Prince Philip	200.00	2010	1st Notes Issued /Bank of Canada	225.00
2008	Royal Canadian Mint	175.00	2012	The Calgary Stampede	275.00

50 DOLLAR SILVER COMMEMORATIVES

2013 The Beaver

2014 Swimming Beaver

2013 Queen's Coronation

Legend of the Spirit Bear

2013 HMS Shannon and USS Chesapeake

2014 Maple Leaves

Date	Description	Buying Price	Date	Description	Buying Price
2013	The Beaver	250.00	2014	Swimming Beaver	250.00
2013	Queen's Coronation	300.00	2014	Legend of the Spirit Bear	250.00
2013	Shannon / Chesapeake	250.00	2014	Maple Leaves	250.00

Note: Coins illustrated on pages 146 and 147 are smaller than actual size.

50 DOLLAR SILVER COMMEMORATIVES

Iconic Polar Bear   Snowy Owl   Beaver

Date	Description	Buying Price	Date	Description	Buying Price
2014	Polar Bear	50.00	2014	Beaver	50.00
2014	Snowy Owl	50.00			

100 DOLLAR SILVER COMMEMORATIVES

2013 Bison Stampede

2014 Rocky Mountain Bighorn Sheep

2014 The Grizzly

2014 100th Anniv. of the Declaration
of the First World War

2014 Majestic Bald Eagle

2014 Majestic Maple Leaves

Date	Description	Buying Price	Date	Description	Buying Price
2013	Bison Stampede	100.00	2014	Rocky Mountain Bighorn Sheep	100.00
2014	The Grizzly	100.00	2014	100th Anniv. First World War	100.00
2014	Majestic Bald Eagle	100.00	2014	Majestic Maple Leaves	100.00

Note: Coins illustrated smaller than actual size.

250 DOLLAR SILVER COMMEMORATIVES

2007 Early Canada

2009 Surviving The Flood

2008 Towards Confederation

2010 The Eagle, Enamel Finish

2009 The Canada of Today

2010 125th Anniv. Banff National Park

Date	Description	Buying Price	Date	Description	Buying Price
2007	Early Canada	1,000.00	2010	The Eagle, Proof Finish	850.00
2008	Towards Confederation	900.00	2010	The Eagle. Enamel Finish	850.00
2009	The Canada of Today	900.00	2010	The Eagle, Antique Finish	850.00
2009	Surviving the Flood	950.00	2010	125th Anniv. Banff National Park	1,000.00

Note: Coins illustrated smaller than actual size.

250 DOLLAR SILVER COMMEMORATIVES

2011 375th Anniv. of the First European
Observation of Lacrosse

2012 Battle of Queenston Heights

2012 Year of the Dragon

2013 Canada's Arctic Landscape

2012 The Moose Family

2013 Year of the Snake

Date	Description	Buying Price	Date	Description	Buying Price
2011	375th Anniv. Lacrosse	1,050.00	2012	Battle of Queenston Heights	1,125.00
2012	Year of the Dragon	1,100.00	2013	Canada's Arctic Landscape	1,125.00
2012	The Moose Family	1,100.00	2013	Year of the Snake	1,125.00

Note: Coins illustrated smaller than actual size.

250 DOLLAR SILVER COMMEMORATIVES

2013 250th Anniv. of the
Seven Years War

2014 Year of the Horse

2013 Battle of Chateauguay

2014 In The Eyes of the Snowy Owl

2013 The Caribou

2014 Battle of Lundy's Lane

Date	Description	Buying Price	Date	Description	Buying Price
2013	Seven Years War	1,125.00	2014	Year of the Horse	1,125.00
2013	Battle of Chateauguay	1,125.00	2014	In the Eyes of the Snowy Owl	1,125.00
2013	The Caribou	1,125.00	2014	Battle of Lundy's Lane	1,125.00
			2015	Year of the Sheep	1,150.00

Note: Coins illustrated smaller than actual size.

GOLD COMMEMORATIVES

ONE CENT GOLD COMMEMORATIVE

Date	Description	Buying Price
2012	The Penny	60.00

25 CENT GOLD COMMEMORATIVES

| Caribou | Cougar | Humming-bird | Bighorn Sheep |

| Eastern Chipmunk | Grizzly Bear | Rock Rabbit |

Date	Description	Buying Price
2010	Caribou	35.00
2011	Cougar	35.00
2013	Hummingbird	35.00
2014	Rocky Mountain Bighorn Sheep	40.00
2014	Eastern Chipmunk	40.00
2015	Grizzly Bear	40.00
2015	Rock Rabbit	40.00

50 CENT GOLD COMMEMORATIVES

| Boreal Forest | Orca Whale | Peregrine Falcon |

| Wood Bison | Caribou Gold Rush | Owl Shaman Holding Goose |

| Bald Eagle | Louisbourg | Starfish |

| Beaver | Osprey | Seahorse |

| Quebec/Charlottetown | Owl | Maple Leaf |

Date	Description	Buying Price
2011	Boreal Forest	65.00
2011	Orca Whale	65.00
2011	Peregrine Falcon	65.00
2011	Wood Bison	65.00
2012	Caribou Gold Rush	65.00
2013	Owl Shaman Holding Goose	65.00
2013	Bald Eagle	65.00
2013	300th Anniv. Louisbourg	65.00
2013	Starfish	65.00
2014	Canada's Classic Beaver	65.00
2014	Osprey	65.00
2014	Seahorse	65.00
2014	Quebec/Charlottetown Conference	65.00
2015	Owl	65.00
2015	Maple Leaf	65.00

GOLD LOUIS COMMEMORATIVES

| 2006 | 2007 | 2008 |

Date	Description	Buying Price
2006	Gold Louis	75.00
2007	Gold Louis	75.00
2008	Gold Louis	75.00

5 DOLLAR GOLD COMMEMORATIVES

Norman Bethune

Royal Cypher

Year of the Dragon

Year of the Snake

Beaver

Polar Bear

Caribou

Wolf

Orca

B ald Eagle

Grizzly Bear

Moose

Nanaboozhoo

Maple Leaves

Cougar

Date	Description	Buying Price
2011	Norman Bethune	150.00
2012	Royal Cypher	150.00
2012	Year of the Dragon	150.00
2013	Year of the Snake	150.00
2013	Beaver	150.00
2013	Polar Bear	150.00
2013	Caribou	150.00
2013	Wolf	150.00
2013	Orca	150.00
2014	Bald Eagle	150.00
2014	Grizzly Bear	150.00
2014	Moose	150.00
2014	Canada Goose	150.00
2014	Bison	150.00
2014	Nanaboozhoo	150.00
2014	Maple Leaves	150.00
2014	Cougar	150.00
2015	Year of the Sheep	150.00

5 and 10 DOLLAR GOLD COMMEMORATIVES

Date	Description	Buying Price
2002	$5 Comm. 1912-2002	360.00
2002	$10 Comm. 1912-2002	720.00

20 DOLLAR GOLD COMMEMORATIVES

Date	Description	Buying Price
1967	Centennial of Confederation	700.00

25 DOLLAR GOLD COMMEMORATIVES

Arctic Fox

Pronghorn

Miss Canada

Wolverine

Date	Description	Buying Price
2013	The Arctic Fox	350.00
2013	Pronghorn	350.00
2013	Miss Canada: An Allegory	350.00
2014	Wolverine	350.00
2014	Pope John Paul II	350.00

50 DOLLAR GOLD COMMEMORATIVES

60th ANNIV. END WWII

Date	Description	Buying Price
2005	60th Anniv. End WWII	325.00

THE QUEEN'S DIAMOND JUBILEE

Queen's Diamond Jubilee
Reverse

Date	Description	Buying Price
2012	The Queen's Diamond Jubilee	1,500.00

UNESCO

Mount Fuji and
Canadian Rockies
Reverse

Date	Description	Buying Price
2015	Mt. Fuji and the Canadian Rockies	350.00

75 DOLLAR GOLD COMMEMORATIVES

POPE JOHN PAUL II

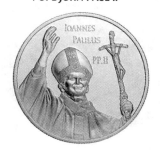

Date	Description	Buying Price
2005	Pope John Paul II	850.00

VANCOUVER 2010 OLYMPIC WINTER GAMES

2007 R.C.M.P.   2007 Athletes' Pride

2007 Canada Geese   2008 Four Host Nations

2008 Home of the Games   2008 Inukshuk

75 DOLLAR GOLD COMMEMORATIVES

VANCOUVER 2010 OLYMPIC WINTER GAMES (cont.)

2009 Wolf   2009 Olympic Spirit

2009 Moose

Date	Description	Buying Price
2007	R.C.M.P.	325.00
2007	Athletes' Pride	325.00
2007	Canada Geese	325.00
2008	Four Host First Nations	325.00
2008	Home of the 2010 Games	325.00
2008	Inukshuk	325.00
2009	Wolf	325.00
2009	Olympic Spirit	325.00
2009	Moose	325.00

FOUR SEASONS MAPLE LEAVES

Spring   Summer

Fall   Winter

Date	Description	Buying Price
2010	Spring Maple Leaves	325.00
2010	Summer Maple Leaves	325.00
2010	Fall Maple Leaves	325.00
2010	Winter Maple Leaves	325.00

WORLD BASEBALL CLASSIC SERIES

Ball Diamond   Hardball

Date	Description	Buying Price
2013	Ball Diamond	375.00
2013	Hardball	375.00

SUPERMAN™

Date	Description	Buying Price
2013	75th Anniv. Superman™	1,500.00

FIFA™ WOMEN'S WORLD CUP

Soccer Ball   Chmpshp. Game

Trophy

Date	Description	Buying Price
2015	Soccer Ball	350.00
2015	Championship Game	350.00
2015	Trophy	350.00

100 DOLLAR GOLD COMMEMORATIVES

Canada issued the first one-hundred-dollar gold coin in 1976 to commemorate the Montreal Olympic Games. In that year two qualities and proportions of fineness were released; uncirculated coins were .585 fine (14 karat), and proof coins were .916 fine (22 karat). From 1976 to 1986, only proof quality coins with a fineness of .916 were issued. In 1987 the quality remained the same (proof), but the fineness of the coin was altered to .583 fine, or 14 karat, again.

IMPORTANT

Proof coins must be in mint-state condition. Mishandled, mounted or damaged coins are discounted from the prices listed. The buying price for gold coins is tied to the market price of gold. Any movement in the gold price will result in a corresponding price movement for these coins.

1976 - 14kt

1976 - 22 kt

1977

1978

1979

1980

1981

1982

1983

1984

Date	Description	Fineness	Buying Price	Date	Description	Fineness	Buying Price
1976	14 kt Olympic	.583	350.00	1980	Arctic Territories	.916	700.00
1976	22 kt Olympic	.916	700.00	1981	"O Canada"	.916	700.00
1977	Jubilee	.916	700.00	1982	Constitution	.916	700.00
1978	Unity	.916	700.00	1983	Gilbert's Landing	.916	700.00
1979	Year of the Child	.916	700.00	1984	Voyage of Discovery	.916	700.00

100 DOLLAR GOLD COMMEMORATIVES

1985   1986   1987   1988

1989   1990   1991   1992

1993   1994   1995   1996

1997   1998   1999   2000

Date	Description	Fineness	Buying Price	Date	Description	Fineness	Buying Price
1985	National Parks	.916	670.00	1993	Horseless Carriage	.583	335.00
1986	Peace	.916	670.00	1994	The Home Front	.583	335.00
1987	Calgary Olympics	.583	335.00	1995	Louisbourg	.583	335.00
1988	Bowhead Whale	.583	335.00	1996	Klondike Gold Rush	.583	335.00
1989	Sainte-Marie	.583	335.00	1997	Bell	.583	335.00
1990	Literacy Year	.583	335.00	1998	Insulin	.583	335.00
1991	Empress of India	.583	335.00	1999	Newfoundland	.583	335.00
1992	Montreal	.583	335.00	2000	Northwest Passage	.583	335.00

100 DOLLAR GOLD COMMEMORATIVES

Date	Description	Fineness	Buying Price	Date	Description	Fineness	Buying Price
2001	Library of Parliament	.583	335.00	2009	Nunavut	.583	300.00
2002	Oil Industry	.583	335.00	2010	Hudson's Bay	.583	300.00
2003	Marquis Wheat	.583	335.00	2011	Canada's First Railroad	.583	300.00
2004	St. Lawrence Seaway	.583	300.00	2012	Caribou Gold Rush	.583	300.00
2005	Supreme Court	.583	300.00	2013	Can. Arctic Expedition	.583	300.00
2006	Hockey	.583	300.00	2014	Quebec/Charlottetown	.583	300.00
2007	Dominion of Canada	.583	300.00	2014	Superman™	.583	300.00
2008	Fraser River	.583	300.00	2015	Sir John A Macdonald	.583	300.00

150 DOLLAR GOLD COMMEMORATIVES

CHINESE LUNAR HOLOGRAM COINS

2000	2001	2002	2003
2004	2005	2006	2007
2008	2009	2010	2011

Date	Description	Buying Price	Date	Description	Buying Price
2000	Year of the Dragon	650.00	2006	Year of the Dog	385.00
2001	Year of the Snake	385.00	2007	Year of the Pig	385.00
2002	Year of the Horse	385.00	2008	Year of the Rat	385.00
2003	Year of the Ram	385.00	2009	Year of the Ox	385.00
2004	Year of the Monkey	385.00	2010	Year of the Tiger	385.00
2005	Year of the Rooster	385.00	2011	Year of the Rabbit	385.00

150 DOLLAR GOLD COMMEMORATIVES

BLESSINGS SERIES

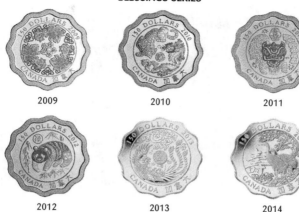

2009   2010   2011

2012   2013   2014

Date	Description	Buying Price	Date	Description	Buying Price
2009	Blessings of Wealth	475.00	2012	Blessings of Good Fortune	475.00
2010	Blessings of Strength	475.00	2013	Blessings of Peace	475.00
2011	Blessings of Happiness	475.00	2014	Blessings of Longevity	475.00

CLASSIC CHINESE LUNAR SERIES

2010   2011   2012   2013

Date	Description	Buying Price	Date	Description	Buying Price
2010	Year of the Tiger	375.00	2013	Year of the Snake	375.00
2011	Year of the Rabbit	375.00	2014	Year of the Horse	375.00
2012	Year of the Dragon	375.00	2015	Year of the Sheep	375.00

175 DOLLAR GOLD COMMEMORATIVE

Date	Description	Buying Price
1992	Olympic Movement	670.00

200 DOLLAR GOLD COMMEMORATIVES

1990	1991	1992	1993
1994	1995	1996	1997
1998	1999	2000	2001
2002	2003	2004	2005

Date	Description	Buying Price	Date	Description	Buying Price
1990	Canada's Flag	670.00	1998	White Buffalo	670.00
1991	A National Passion	670.00	1999	Mikmaq Butterfly	670.00
1992	Niagara Falls	670.00	2000	Mother and Child	670.00
1993	RCMP	670.00	2001	Cornelius Krieghoff	670.00
1994	Anne of Green Gables	670.00	2002	Tom Thompson	670.00
1995	Sugar Bush	670.00	2003	Lionel Fitzgerald	670.00
1996	Transcontinental Landscape	670.00	2004	Alfred Pellan	630.00
1997	Haida	670.00	2005	Fur Trade	630.00

200 DOLLAR GOLD COMMEMORATIVES

2006 Timber Trade

2007 Fishing Trade

2008 Agriculture Trade

2009 Mining Trade

2010 First Canadian
Olympic Gold Medal

2010 Petrolium and
Oil Trade

2011 S.S. Beaver

2011 Duke and Duchess
of Cambrudge

2011 Wayne and
Walter Gretzky

2012 The Vikings

2012 The Challenge

2013 Jacques Cartier

2013 Grandmother Moon
Mask

2014 Samuel de
Champlain

2014 Royal Generations

2014 Matriarch Moon
Mask

Date	Description	Buying Price
2006	Timber Trade	630.00
2007	Fishing Trade	630.00
2008	Agriculture Trade	630.00
2009	Mining Trade	630.00
2010	1st Canadian Olympic Gold Medal	630.00
2010	Petroleum and Oil Trade	630.00
2011	S.S. Beaver	630.00
2011	Duke and Duchess of Cambridge	630.00

Date	Description	Buying Price
2011	Wayne and Walter Gretzky	630.00
2012	The Vikings	630.00
2012	The Challenge	630.00
2013	Jacques Cartier	630.00
2013	Grandmother Moon Mask	630.00
2014	Samuel de Champlain	630.00
2014	Royal Generations	630.00
2014	Matriarch Moon Mask	630.00

200 DOLLAR GOLD COMMEMORATIVES

2014 75th Anniv.
Royal Visit

2014 Fierce Can. Lynx

2014 Interconnections:
Land - Beaver

2014 Interconnections:
Air - Thunderbird

2014 Interconnections:
Sea - Orca

2014 "Zunoqua"
Emily Carr

2015 Henry Hudson

2015 Singing Moon Mask

2015 Largemouth Bass

Date	Description	Buying Price
2014	75th Anniv. Royal Visit	1,500.00
2014	Fierce Canadian Lynx	1,500.00
2014	Interconnections: Land - Beaver	1,500.00
2014	Interconnections: Air - Thunderbird	1,500.00
2014	Interconnections: Sea - Orca	1,500.00

Date	Description	Buying Price
2014	"Zunoqua" - Emily Carr	1,500.00
2015	Henry Hudson	1,500.00
2015	Singing Moon Mask	1,500.00
2015	Largemouth Bass	1,500.00

250 DOLLAR GOLD COMMEMORATIVES

14 KARAT (.583) GOLD

2006 Dog Sled Team

Date	Description	Buying Price
2006	Dog Sled Team	850.00

24 KARAT (.9999) GOLD

2014 Canadian Contemporary Art

2014 75th Anniv. of the Declaration
of the Second World Ware

2014 100th Anniv. of the Completion of
the Grand Trunk Pacific Railway

Date	Description	Buying Price
2014	Canadian Contemporary Art	3,000.00
2014	75th Anniv. Declaration WWII	3,000.00
2014	Grand Trunk Pacific Railway	3,000.00

300 DOLLAR GOLD COMMEMORATIVES

14 KARAT (.583) GOLD, LARGE SIZE (50 mm)

2002 Triple Cameo Portraits

2005 The 1870 Shinplaster

2003 Great Seal of Canada

2006 The 1900 Shinplaster

2004 Arms of Canada / Quadruple Cameo

2006 The 1923 Shinplaster

Date	Description	Buying Price	Date	Description	Buying Price
2002	Triple Cameo Portraits	1,600.00	2005	The 1870 Shinplaster	1,600.00
2003	Great Seal of Canada	1,600.00	2006	The 1900 Shinplaster	1,600.00
2004	Quadruple Cameo Portraits	1,600.00	2007	The 1923 Shinplaster	1,600.00

300 DOLLAR GOLD COMMEMORATIVES

14 KARAT (.583) GOLD, LARGE SIZE (50 mm)

2006 Crystal Snowflake

2007 Four Seasons Moon Mask

2006 80th Birthday Queen Elizabeth II

2008 (Olympic) Competition

2007 Olympic Ideals

2008 Newfoundland/Labrador Arms

Date	Description	Buying Price	Date	Description	Buying Price
2006	Crystal Snowflake	1,525.00	2007	Four Seasons Moon Mask	1,525.00
2006	80th Birthday Elizabeth II	1,525.00	2008	Competition	1,525.00
2007	Olympic Ideals	1,525.00	2008	Nfld. / Labrador Arms	1,525.00

300 DOLLAR GOLD COMMEMORATIVES

14 KARAT (.583) GOLD, LARGE SIZE (50 mm)

2008 Alberta Arms

2009 (Olympic) Friendship

2009 Yukon Territory Arms

2009 Summer Moon Mask

2009 Prince Edward Island Arms

2010 Crystal Snowflake

Date	Description	Buying Price	Date	Description	Buying Price
2008	Alberta Arms	1,525.00	2009	(Olympic) Friendship	1,525.00
2009	Yukon Territory Arms	1,525.00	2009	Summer Moon Mask	1,525.00
2009	Prince Edward Island Arms	1,525.00	2010	Crystal Snowflake	1,525.00

300 DOLLAR GOLD COMMEMORATIVES

14 KARAT (.583) GOLD, LARGE SIZE (50 mm)

2010 British Columbia Arms

2011 Nova Scotia Arms

2010 New Brunswick Arms

2012 Quebec Arms

2011 Manitoba Arms

2012 Nunavut

Date	Description	Buying Price
2010	British Columbia Arms	1,525.00
2010	New Brunswick Arms	1,525.00
2011	Manitoba Arms	1,525.00

Date	Description	Buying Price
2011	Nova Scotia Arms	1,525.00
2012	Quebec Arms	1,525.00
2012	Nunavut	1,525.00

300 DOLLAR GOLD COMMEMORATIVES

2013 Ontario

2014 Saskatchewan

2013 Northwest Territories

2014 Canada

14 KARAT (.583) GOLD, LARGE SIZE (50 mm)

Date	Description	Buying Price	Date	Description	Buying Price
2013	Ontario	1,525.00	2014	Saskatchewan	1,525.00
2013	Northwest Territores	1,525.00	2014	Canada	1,525.00

Note: Coins illustrated on pages 166 to 170 illustrated smaller than actual size.

300 DOLLAR GOLD COMMEMORATIVES

14 KARAT (.583) GOLD, SMALL SIZE (40 mm)

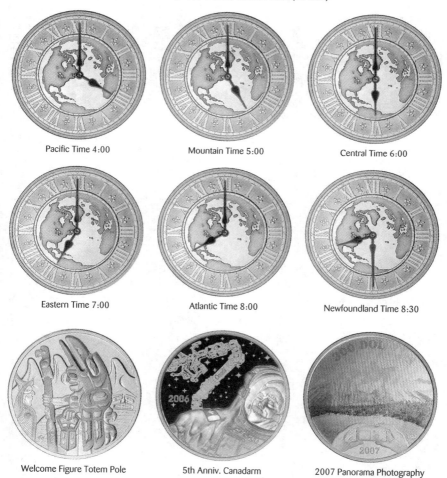

Pacific Time 4:00

Mountain Time 5:00

Central Time 6:00

Eastern Time 7:00

Atlantic Time 8:00

Newfoundland Time 8:30

Welcome Figure Totem Pole

5th Anniv. Canadarm

2007 Panorama Photography

Date	Description	Buying Price	Date	Description	Buying Price
2005	Pacific Time 4:00	1,125.00	2005	Newfoundland Time 8:30	1,125.00
2005	Mountain Time 5:00	1,125.00	2005	Welcome Figure Totem Pole	1,125.00
2005	Central Time 6:00	1,125.00	2006	5th Anniv. Canadarm	1,125.00
2005	Eastern Time 7:00	1,125.00	2007	Panorama Photography	1,125.00
2005	Atlantic Time 8:00	1,125.00	2008	IMAX©	1,125.00

Note: 1. Coins illustrated smaller than actual size.
        2. The IMAX© $300 gold coin is not illustrated.

350 DOLLAR GOLD COMMEMORATIVES
24 KARAT (.99999) GOLD

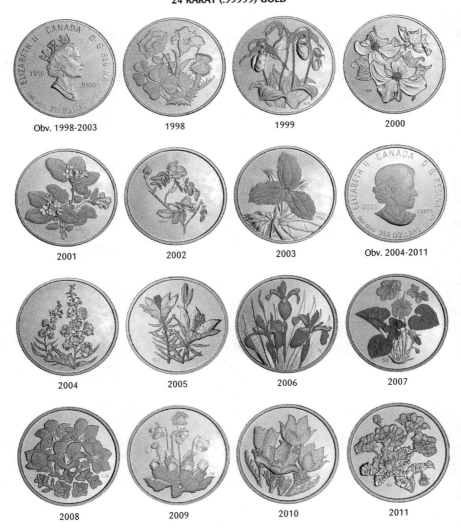

Obv. 1998-2003   1998   1999   2000

2001   2002   2003   Obv. 2004-2011

2004   2005   2006   2007

2008   2009   2010   2011

Date	Description	Buying Price	Date	Description	Buying Price
1998	90th Anniv. R.C.M.	1,650.00	2005	Western Red Lily, Saskatchewan	1,525.00
1999	Golden Slipper, P.E.I.	1,650.00	2006	Iris Versicolor, Quebec	1,525.00
2000	Pacific Dogwood, B.C.	1,650.00	2007	Purple Violet, N.B.	1,525.00
2001	Mayflower, N.S.	1,650.00	2008	Purple Saxifrage, Nunavut	1,525.00
2002	Wild Rose, Alberta	1,650.00	2009	Pitcher Plant, Nfld. & Labrador	1,525.00
2003	Trillium, Ontario	1,650.00	2010	Prairie Crocus, Manitoba	1,525.00
2004	Fireweed, Yukon	1,525.00	2011	Mountain Avers, NWT	1,525.00

500 DOLLAR GOLD COMMEMORATIVES
24 KARAT (.9999) GOLD

60th Wedding Anniversary
Queen Qlizabeth /Prince Philip

100th Anniversary of the
Royal Canadian Mint

150th Anniv. Start of Construction of the
Parliament Buildings

75th Anniv. of First Bank Notes
Issued by the Bank of Canada

100th Anniv. First Canadian Gold Coin

Calgary Stampede

Date	Description	Buying Price
2007	60th Wedding Anniv.	6,750.00
2008	100th Anniv. RCM	6,750.00
2009	150th Anniv. Parliament Bldgs	6,750.00

Date	Description	Buying Price
2010	75th Anniv. Bank of Canada	6,750.00
2012	100th Anniv. First Can. Gold	6,750.00
2012	Calgary Stampede	6,750.00

500 DOLLAR GOLD COMMEMORATIVES

24 KARAT (.9999) GOLD

Maple Leaf Forever

An Aboriginal Story

HMS Shannon / USS Chesapeake

Legend of the Spirit Bear

Date	Description	Buying Price	Date	Description	Buying Price
2012	Maple Leaf Forever	6,750.00	2013	An Aboriginal Story	6,750.00
2013	Shannon/Chesapeake	6,750.00	2014	Legend of the Spirit Bear	6,750.00

Note: Coins illustrated on pages 172-177 are smaller than actual size.

2,500 DOLLAR GOLD COMMEMORATIVES

24 KARAT (.9999) GOLD

2007 Early Canada

2009 Surviving the Flood

2008 Towards Confederation

2010 The Eagle

2009 The Canada of Today

2010 Banff National Park

Date	Description	Buying Price
2007	Early Canada	43,500.00
2008	Towards Confederations	43,500.00
2009	The Canada of Today	43,500.00

Date	Description	Buying Price
2009	Surviving the Flood	43,500.00
2010	The Eagle	43,500.00
2010	Banff National Park	43,500.00

2,500 DOLLAR GOLD COMMEMORATIVES

24 Karat (.9999) GOLD

2011 375th Anniv. Lacrosse

2012 Year of the Dragon (Classic)

2012 The Challenge

2012 Battle of Queenston Heights

2012 Year of the Dragon

2013 250th Anniversary of the
end of the Seven Years War

Date	Description	Buying Price
2011	375th Anniv. Lacrosse	43,500.00
2012	The Challenge	43,500.00
2012	Year of the Dragon	43,500.00

Date	Description	Buying Price
2012	Year of the Dragon (Classic)	43,500.00
2012	Battle of Queenston Heights	43,500.00
2013	250th Anniv. Seven Years War	43,500.00

2,500 DOLLAR GOLD COMMEMORATIVES

24 KARAT (.9999) GOLD

2013 Year of the Snake

2013 The Caribou

2013 Canada's Arctic Landscape

2014 Year of the Horse

2013 Battle of Crysler's Farm and
Battle of Chateauguay

2014 In The Eyes of the Snowy Owl

Date	Description	Buying Price	Date	Description	Buying Price
2013	Year of the Snake	43,500.00	2013	The Caribou	43,500.00
2013	Canada's Arctic Landscape	43,500.00	2014	Year of the Horse	43,500.00
2013	Battle Crysler's Farm	43,500.00	2014	In the Eyes of the Snowy Owl	43,500.00

2,500 DOLLAR GOLD COMMEMORATIVES

24 KARAT (.9999) GOLD

2014 Battle of Lundy's Lane

2015 Year of the Sheep

Date	Description	Buying Price	Date	Description	Buying Price
2014	Battle of Lundy's Lane	43,500.00	2015	Year of the Sheep	43,500.00

Note: Coins illustrated smaller than actual size.

PALLADIUM COMMEMORATIVES

FIFTY DOLLAR COMMEMORATIVES
1 Troy Ounce (.9995) Palladium

BIG AND LITTLE BEAR CONSTELLATIONS

Spring

Autumn

Summer

Winter

Date	Description	Buying Price	Date	Description	Buying Price
2006	Spring	700.00	2006	Autumn	700.00
2006	Summer	700.00	2006	Winter	700.00

PLATINUM COMMEMORATIVES
300 HUNDRED DOLLAR COMMEMORATIVES
1 Troy Ounce (.9995) Platinum

2007 Wooly Mammoth

2008 Scimitar Cat

2009 Steppe Bison

2010 Ground Sloth

2011 Cougar

2012 Maple Leaf Forever

2012 The Bull Moose

2013 The Bald Eagle

2013 Rocky Mountain Bighorn Sheep

2013 Shannon/Chesapeake

2013 25th Anniv. Maple Leaf

2014 Bison

Date	Description	Buying Price	Date	Description	Buying Price
2007	Woolly Mammoth	1,300.00	2012	The Bull Moose	1,300.00
2008	Scimitar Cat	1,300.00	2013	The Bald Eagle	1,300.00
2009	Steppe Bison	1,300.00	2013	Rocky Mountain Bighorn Sheep	1,300.00
2010	Ground Sloth	1,300.00	2013	HMS Shannon/USS Chesapeake	1,300.00
2011	Cougar	1,300.00	2013	25th Anniv. Pt. Maple Leaf	1,300.00
2012	Maple Leaf Forever	1,300.00	2014	Bison	1,300.00

300 HUNDRED DOLLAR COMMEMORATIVES
1 Troy Ounce (.9995) Platinum

2014 Maple Leaf Forever

2014 "A Skidegate Beaver Pole" Emily Carr

2015 Grizzly Bear

2015 Maple Leaf Forever

2015 Rainbow Trout

2015 White-tailed Deer

Date	Description	Buying Price	Date	Description	Buying Price
2014	Maple Leaf Forever	1,500.00	2015	Maple Leaf Forever	1,500.00
2014	Maple Leaf Forever	1,500.00	2015	Rainbow Trout	1,500.00
2014	"Skidegate Beaver Pole" E. Carr	1,500.00	2015	White-tailed Deer	1,500.00
2015	Grizzly Bear	1,500.00			

PROOF PLATINUM COMMEMORATIVE SETS

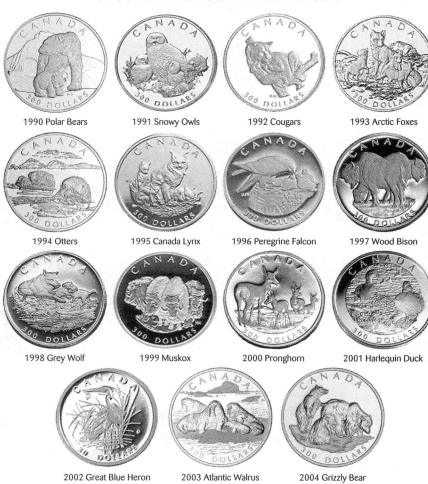

1990 Polar Bears   1991 Snowy Owls   1992 Cougars   1993 Arctic Foxes

1994 Otters   1995 Canada Lynx   1996 Peregrine Falcon   1997 Wood Bison

1998 Grey Wolf   1999 Muskox   2000 Pronghorn   2001 Harlequin Duck

2002 Great Blue Heron   2003 Atlantic Walrus   2004 Grizzly Bear

Date	Description	Buying Price	Date	Description	Buying Price
1990	Polar Bear Set	2,200.00	1997	Wood Bison $30	120.00
1991	Snowy Owl Set	2,200.00	1997	Wood Bison $150	1,200.00
1992	Cougar Set	2,200.00	1998	Grey Wolf Set	2,200.00
1993	Arctic Foxes Set	2,200.00	1998	Grey Wolf $30	120.00
1994	Sea Otters Set	2,200.00	1998	Grey Wolf $150	1,200.00
1995	Canada Lynx Set	2,200.00	1999	Muskox Set	2,200.00
1995	Canada Lynx $30	120.00	1999	Muskox $30	120.00
1995	Canada Lynx $150	1,200.00	2000	Pronghorn Set	2,200.00
1996	Peregrine Falcon Set	2,200.00	2001	Harlequin Duck Set	2,200.00
1996	Peregrine Falcon $30	120.00	2002	Great Blue Heron Set	2,200.00
1996	Peregrine Falcon $150	1,200.00	2003	Atlantic Walrus Set	2,200.00
1997	Wood Bison Set	2,200.00	2004	Grizzly Bear Set	2,200.00

Note: The Platinum Proof Set contains four coins: $300., $150., $75. and $30.

COLLECTOR SETS

Listed on this and the following page are the Collector sets of coins issued by the Royal Canadian Mint between the years 1954 and 2014.

SIX COIN PROOF-LIKE AND BRILLIANT UNCIRCULATED SETS

6-COIN SILVER PROOF-LIKE SETS

Date	Description	Buying Price
1954	Voyageur	325.00
1955	Voyageur	225.00
1955	Arnprior	300.00
1956	Voyageur	135.00
1957	Voyageur	80.00
1958	British Columbia	65.00
1959	Voyageur	30.00
1960	Voyageur	25.00
1961	Voyageur	17.50
1962	Voyageur	17.50
1963	Voyageur	17.50
1964	Charlottetown	17.50
1965	Voyageur	17.50
1966	Voyageur	17.50
1967	Centennial	17.50

6-COIN NICKEL BRILLIANT UNCIRCULATED SETS

Date	Description	Buying Price
1968	Voyageur	2.00
1969	Voyageur	2.00
1970	Manitoba	2.00
1971	British Columbia	2.00
1972	Voyageur	2.00
1973	R.C.M.P., Small Bust	2.00
1973	R.C.M.P., Large Bust	150.00
1974	Winnipeg	2.00
1975	Voyageur	2.00
1976	Voyageur	2.00
1977	Voyageur	2.00
1978	Voyageur	2.00
1979	Voyageur	2.00

6-COIN NICKEL BRILLIANT UNCIRCULATED SETS

Date	Description	Buying Price
1980	Voyageur	2.00
1981	Voyageur	2.00
1982	Voyageur	2.00
1983	Voyageur	2.50
1984	Voyageur	2.50
1985	Voyageur	2.50
1986	Voyageur	2.50
1987	Voyageur	2.50
1988	Loon	2.50
1989	Loon	4.00
1990	Loon	4.00
1991	Loon	10.00
1992	Loon	5.00
1993	Loon	2.00
1994	Loon	2.50
1995	Loon	2.50
1996	Loon	10.00

BUNDLE OF JOY
6-COIN NICKEL BRILLIANT UNCIRCULATED SETS

Date	Description	Buying Price
1995	Loon	6.00
1996	Loon	6.00

OH CANADA!
6-COIN NICKEL BRILLIANT UNCIRCULATED SETS

Date	Description	Buying Price
1994	Loon	4.00
1995	Loon	4.00
1996	Loon	7.00

SEVEN COIN BRILLIANT UNCIRCULATED SETS

7- COIN NICKEL SETS

Date	Description	Buying Price
1997	Loon/Polar Bear	4.00
1998	Loon/Polar Bear	8.00
1998W	Loon/Polar Bear	8.00
1999	Loon/Polar Bear	4.00
1999	Loon/Nunavut	4.00
2000	Loon/Knowledge	4.00
2000W	Loon/Polar Bear	4.00

MULTI-PLY PLATED STEEL SETS

Date	Description	Buying Price
2001P	Loon/Polar Bear	4.00
2002P	Loon/Polar Bear	8.00
2003P	Loon/Polar Bear	10.00
2004P	Loon/Polar Bear	10.00
2005P	Loon/Polar Bear	8.00
2006P	Loon/Polar Bear	8.00
2007	Loon/Polar Bear	9.00
2008	Loon/Polar Bear	9.00
2009	Loon/Polar Bear	9.00
2010	Loon/Polar Bear	9.00
2011	Loon/Polar Bear	9.00
2012	Loon/Polar Bear	9.00

BUNDLE OF JOY/TINY TREASURES SETS - NICKEL

Date	Description	Buying Price
1997	Loon/Polar Bear	5.00
1998	Loon/Polar Bear	5.00
1998W	Loon/Polar Bear	5.00
1999	Loon/Polar Bear	5.00
2000	Loon/Polar Bear	5.00
2000W	Loon/Polar Bear	5.00

TINY TREASURES SETS - MULTI-PLY PLATED STEEL

Date	Description	Buying Price
2001P	Loon/Polar Bear	5.00
2002P	Loon/Polar Bear	5.00
2003P	Loon/Polar Bear	5.00

BABY GIFT SETS - MULTI-PLY PLATED STEEL

Date	Description	Buying Price
2004P	Loon/Polar Bear	5.00
2005P	Loon/Polar Bear	5.00

BIRTHDAY GIFT SETS MULTI-PLY PLATED STEEL

Date	Description	Buying Price
2004P	Loon/Polar Bear	8.00
2005P	Loon/Polar Bear	8.00

GRADUATION GIFT SETS MULTI-PLY PLATED STEEL

Date	Description	Buying Price
2004P	Loon/Polar Bear	8.00
2005P	Loon/Polar Bear	8.00

HOLIDAY GIFT SETS MULTI-PLY PLATED STEEL

Date	Description	Buying Price
2004P	Loon/Polar Bear	5.00
2005P	Loon/Polar Bear	5.00

OH! CANADA! GIFT SETS MULTI-PLY PLATED STEEL

Date	Description	Buying Price
1997	Flying Loon/Polar Bear	15.00
1998	Loon/Polar Bear	6.00
1998W	Loon/Polar Bear	6.00
1999	Loon/Polar Bear	5.00
2000	Loon/Polar Bear	5.00
2000W	Loon/Polar Bear	5.00
2001P	Loon/Polar Bear	5.00
2002P	Loon/Polar Bear	5.00
2003P	Loon/Polar Bear	5.00
2004P	Loon/Polar Bear	5.00
2005P	Loon/Polar Bear	5.00

SEVEN COIN UNCIRCULATED SETS

MULTI-PLY PLATED STEEL

BABY GIFT SETS

Date	Description	Buying Price
2006P	Loon/Polar Bear	5.00
2007	Loon/Polar Bear	5.00
2008	Loon/Polar Bear	5.00
2009	Loon/Polar Bear	5.00
2010	Loon/Polar Bear	5.00
2011	Loon/Polar Bear	5.00
2012	Loon/Polar Bear	5.00
2013	Loon/Polar Bear	5.00
2014	Stork/Polar Bear	5.00
2015	Teddy Bear/Polar Bear	5.00

HAPPY BIRTHDAY
JOYEUX ANNIVERSAIRE
2006

2006 Birthday Gift Set

BIRTHDAY GIFT SETS

Date	Description	Buying Price
2006P	Loon/Polar Bear	5.00
2007	Loon/Polar Bear	5.00
2008	Loon/Polar Bear	5.00
2011	Loon/Polar Bear	5.00
2012	Loon/Polar Bear	5.00
2013	Loon/Polar Bear	5.00
2014	Gifts/Polar Bear	5.00
2015	Balloons/Polar Bear	5.11

CONGRATULATIONS GIFT SETS

Date	Description	Buying Price
2006P	Loon/Polar Bear	5.00
2007	Loon/Polar Bear	5.00
2008	Loon/Polar Bear	5.00

HOLIDAY GIFT SETS

Date	Description	Buying Price
2006P	Loon/Polar Bear	5.00
2007	Loon/Polar Bear	5.00
2008	Loon/Polar Bear	5.00
2009	Loon/Polar Bear	5.00
2010	Loon/Polar Bear	5.00
2011	Loon/Polar Bear	5.00
2012	Loon/Polar Bear	5.00
2013	Loon/Polar Bear	5.00
2014	Reindeer/Polar Bear	5.00

NHL GIFT SETS

Date	Description	Buying Price
2006P	Loon/Polar Bear	6.00
2007	Loon/Polar Bear	6.00
2008	Loon/Polar Bear	6.00
2009	Loon/Polar Bear	6.00

OH! CANADA! GIFT SETS

Date	Description	Buying Price
2006P	Loon/Polar Bear	8.00
2007	Loon/Polar Bear	8.00
2008	Loon/Polar Bear	8.00
2009	Loon/Polar Bear	8.00
2010	Loon/Polar Bear	8.00
2011	Loon/Polar Bear	8.00
2012	Loon/Polar Bear	8.00
2013	Loon/Polar Bear	8.00
2014	Maple Leaf/Polar Bear	8.00
2015	Maple Leaf/Polar Bear	5.00

WEDDING GIFT SETS

Date	Description	Buying Price
2004P	Loon/Polar Bear	5.00
2005P	Loon/Polar Bear	5.00
2006P	Loon/Polar Bear	5.00
2007	Loon/Polar Bear	5.00
2008	Loon/Polar Bear	5.00
2010	Loon/Polar Bear	5.00
2011	Loon/Polar Bear	5.00
2012	Loon Polar Bear	5.00
2013	Loon/Polar Bear	5.00
2014	Two Turtle Doves/Polar Bear	5.00
2015	Two Swans/Polar Bear	5.00

SPECIAL EDITION BRILLIANT UNCIRCULATED SETS

7-COIN SETS

Date	Description	Buying Price
2002P	Diadem Portrait	7.00
2003WP	Mature Portrait	7.00
2005P	Alberta/Saskatchwan	8.00
2006	10th Anniversary Two Dollars	7.00

11-COIN SETS

Date	Description	Buying Price
2007	Winter Olympics	10.00
2008	Winter Olympics	10.00
2009	Winter Olympics	10.00
2010	Golden Moments	10.00

SPECIAL EDITION UNCIRCULATED SETS

8-COIN SETS

Date	Description	Buying Price
2010	Navy/Sask. Roughriders	10.00
2010	Remembrance Day Poppy	10.00

8-COIN SETS

Date	Description	Buying Price
2011	Parks Canada	15.00

SPECIMEN SETS

SPECIMEN 7-COIN SETS (Double Cent Sets)

Date	Description	Buying Price
1971	Voyageur	3.00
1972	Voyageur	3.00
1973	Voyageur/RCMP, Small Bust	3.00
1973	Voyageur/RCMP, Large Bust	125.00
1974	Voyaguer	3.00
1975	Voyageur	3.00
1976	Voyageur	3.00
1977	Voyageur	3.00
1978	Voyageur	3.00
1979	Voyageur	3.00
1980	Voyageur	3.00

6-COIN SETS (One Cent to One Dollar)

Date	Description	Buying Price
1981	Voyageur	3.50
1982	Voyageur	3.50
1983	Voyageur	3.50
1984	Voyageur	3.50
1985	Voyageur	3.50
1986	Voyageur	3.50
1987	Voyageur	3.50
1988	Loon	3.50
1989	Loon	4.00

SPECIMEN 6-COIN SETS (One Cent to One Dollar)

Date	Description	Buying Price
1990	Loon	4.00
1991	Loon	16.00
1992	Loon	7.00
1993	Loon	4.00
1994	Loon	4.00
1995	Loon	4.00
1996	Loon	10.00

SPECIMEN 6 or 7-COIN SETS

Date	Description	Buying Price
1997	Flying Loon/Polar Bear	15.00
1998	Loon/Polar Bear	6.00
1999	Loon/Polar Bear	6.00
2000	Loon/Polar Bear	6.00
2000	Loon/Polar Bears	6.00
2001P	Loon/Polar Bear	6.00
2002P	Loon Family/Polar Bear	10.00
2003P	Loon/Polar Bear	10.00
2004P	Canada Goose/Polar Bear	20.00
2005P	Tufted Puffin/Polar Bear	25.00
2006P	Snowy Owl/Polar Bear	25.00
2007	Trumpeter Swan/ Polar Bear	20.00
2008	Eider Duck/Polar Bear	20.00
2009	Great Blue Heron/Polar Bear	20.00
2010	Northern Harrier/Polar Bear	20.00
2011	Great Gey Owl/Polar Bear	20.00
2012	Loon with Chicks/Polar Bear	20.00
2013	Blue-Winged Teal/Polar Bear	20.00
2014	Ferruginous Hawk/Polar Bear	20.00
2015	Blue Jay/Polar Bear	20.00

SPECIAL EDITION SPECIMEN SETS

7-COIN SETS

Date	Description	Buying Price
1967	$20 Gold	650.00
1967	Silver Medallion	30.00
2010	Lynx Kittens	20.00
2011	Elk Calf	20.00

7-COIN SETS

Date	Description	Buying Price
2012	Wolf Cubs	20.00
2013	Black Bear Cubs	20.00
2014	Baby Bunnies	20.00
2015	Racoon	20.00

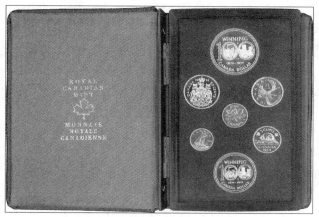

1974 Prestige Set

7-COIN PRESTIGE SETS

Date	Description	Buying Price
1971	British Columbia	7.00
1972	Voyageur	15.00
1973	R.C.M.P., Small Bust	10.00
1973	R.C.M.P., Large Bust	150.00
1974	Winnipeg	10.00
1975	Calgary	10.00

7-COIN PRESTIGE SETS

Date	Description	Buying Price
1976	Parliament	10.00
1977	Jubilee	10.00
1978	Commonwealth Games	10.00
1979	Griffon	10.00
1980	Polar Bear	10.00

PROOF SETS 1981-2015

1997 Proof Set

7-COIN PROOF SETS

Date	Description	Buying Price
1981	Trans Canada	10.00
1982	Regina	10.00
1983	University Games	10.00
1984	Toronto	10.00
1985	National Parks	10.00
1986	Vancouver	10.00
1987	Davis Straits	10.00
1988	Ironworks	10.00
1989	MacKenzie River	12.00
1990	Henry Kelsey	14.00
1991	Frontenac	25.00
1992	Stagecoach	18.00
1993	Hockey	13.00
1994	RCMP	15.00
1994	RCMP, Red Box	15.00
1995	Hudson's Bay	15.00
1995	Hudson's Bay, Red Box	15.00
1996	John McIntosh	20.00
1997	Canada/Russia Hockey	40.00
1998	RCMP 125th Anniversary	40.00

8-COIN PROOF SETS

Date	Description	Buying Price
1999	Juan Perez	40.00
2000	Discovery	40.00
2001	Ballet	40.00
2002	Jubilee	40.00
2003	Cobalt	40.00
2004	Ste Croix	40.00
2005	Canadian Flag	50.00
2006	Victoria Cross	45.00
2007	Thayendanegea	45.00
2008	Quebec City	45.00
2009	Flight in Canada	45.00
2010	Corvette	45.00
2011	Parks Canada	50.00
2011	100th Anniv. 1911 Silver Dollar	50.00
2012	War of 1812	50.00
2012	War of 1812, Premium Set	100.00
2013	Arctic Expedition, Premium Set	100.00
2014	Declaration of WW1, Premium Set	100.00
2014	Start of World War One	50.00
2015	Canadian Flag	50.00
2015	Canadian Flag, Premium Set	115.00

MAPLE LEAF BULLION COINS

The Maple Leaf gold coins were first produced in 1979, the fractional or small sizes three years later in 1982, and the half-ounce size in 1986. In 1988 the four sizes; $5.00, $10.00, $20.00 and $50.00, of platinum were added. Expanding the range in 1993, $1.00 gold and platinum coins were issued, and again in 1994 $2.00 coins were placed on the market.

The price of Maple Leaf bullion coins is based on the spot market price in Canadian dollars on the day of purchase or sale, times their precious metal content, less a small handling charge.

| $50 | $20 | $10 | $5 |

COIN SPECIFICATIONS

Denomination	Description	Content	Weight Tr. Oz.
$1	1/20 Maple	Gold or platinum	.050
$2	1/15 Maple	Gold or platinum	.067
$5	1/10 Maple	Gold or platinum	.100
$10	1/4 Maple	Gold or platinum	.250
$20	1/2 Maple	Gold or platinum	.500
$50	Maple	Gold or platinum	1.00
$5	Maple	Silver	1.00

PRICING EXAMPLE

On September 4th, 2015, the precious metal value of gold and silver in Canadian dollars was $1,491.50 and $19.40 per ounce respectively.

At that rate a fifty dollar gold maple leaf would be worth $1,491.50. A one-tenth maple would be worth 0.10 times $1,491.50, or $149.15.

The same reasoning applies to the value of silver bullion. However, there may be a small discount below bullion value to cover handling charges for dealer buying.

MAPLE LEAF PROOF BULLION ISSUES OF 1989

To commemorate the tenth anniversary of the Maple Leaf bullion program, the Royal Canadian Mint, in 1989, issued a series of proof condition silver, gold and platinum coins, individually and in sets. The single coins and sets were packaged in solid maple presentation cases with brown velvet liners.

Type	Description	Buying Price
Sets	Gold 4 coins: 1, 1/2, 1/4, 1/10 ounce maples	2,500.00
	Platinum 4 coins: 1, 1/2, 1/4, 1/10 ounce maples	2,175.00
	Gold and Platinum 1/10 ounce maple each, Silver 1 ounce maple; 3 coins	270.00
	Gold, Platinum and Silver, 3 coins: 1 ounce maple each	2,525.00
Singles	Gold, One Maple	1,350.00
	Silver, One Maple	22.00

PAPER MONEY OF CANADA

PROVINCE OF CANADA

1866 ISSUES

Denom.	Issue Date	VG Buying Price	Denom.	Issue Date	VG Buying Price
$1	1866	1,200.00	$10	1866	10,000.00
$2	1866	2,200.00	$20	1866	15,000.00
$5	1866	5,000.00	$50	1866	15,000.00

CANADA

1870 ISSUES

Plain   Series Letter A   Series Letter B

Denom.	Issue Date	VG Buying Price	Denom.	Issue Date	VG Buying Price
25-cent Plain	1870	18.00	25-cent Series B	1870	20.00
25-cent Series A	1870	150.00			

Note: The buying prices listed are for notes in **Very Good (VG)** condition. Holed or torn notes wiil be discounted

1870 ISSUES

Denom.	Issue Date	Variety/Signature	VG Buying Price
$1	1870	Payable at Montreal or Toronto	550.00
$1	1870	Payable at Halifax	2,250.00
$1	1870	Payable at St. John	2,250.00
$2	1870	Payable at Montreal or Toronto	2,250.00
$2	1870	Payable at Halifax or St. John	3,000.00

1878 ISSUES

Denom.	Issue Date	Variety/Signature	VG Buying Price
$1	1878	Scalloped Frame, Payable at Montreal or Toronto	450.00
$1	1878	Scalloped Frame, Payable at St. John or Halifax	1,300.00
$1	1878	Lettered Frame, Payable at Montreal or Toronto	150.00
$1	1878	Lettered Frame, Payable at St. John or Halifax	1,850.00
$2	1878	Payable at Montreal or Toronto	1,500.00
$2	1878	Payable at St. John or Halifax	4,000.00

1882 AND 1887 ISSUES

Denom.	Issue Date	Variety/Signature	VG Buying Price
$4	1882		1,100.00
$2	1887	Plain,	500.00
$2	1887	Series A	2,100.00

Note: The buying prices listed are for notes in **Very Good (VG)** condition. Holed or torn notes will be discounted.

1897 AND 1898 ISSUES

No "One" 1897   Inward "One" 1898   Outward "One" 1898

Denom.	Issue Date	Variety/Signature	VG Buying Price
$1	1897	Green face tint	250.00
$2	1897	Red-brown back	2,750.00
$2	1897	Dark brown back	160.00
$1	1898	Inward "One"	70.00
$1	1898	Outward "One"	80.00

1900 AND 1902 ISSUES

"4" on Top   "Four" on Top

Denom.	Issue Date	Variety/Signature	VG Buying Price
25-cent	1900	Courtney	5.00
25-cent	1900	Bouville	5.00
25-cent	1900	Saunders	5.00
$4	1900		500.00
$4	1902	"4" on Top	1.000.00
$4	1902	"Four" on Top	400.00

Note: The buying prices listed are for notes in **Very Good (VG)** condition. Holed or torn notes will be discounted.

1911 AND 1912 ISSUES

| No Seal | Seal over Five | Seal Only |

Denom.	Issue Date	Variety/Signature	VG Buying Price
$1	1911	Green Line or Black Line	55.00
$500	1911		75,000.00
$1,000	1911		75,000.00
$5	1912	No Seal	500.00
$5	1912	Seal over Five	475.00
$5	1912	Seal Only	450.00

1914 AND 1917 ISSUES

Denom.	Issue Date	Variety/Signature	VG Buying Price
$2	1914	No Seal	65.00
$2	1914	Seal over Two	90.00
$2	1914	Seal Only	100.00
$1	1917	No Seal	35.00
$1	1917	Seal over One	40.00
$1	1917	Black Seal	35.00

Note: The buying prices listed are for notes in **Very Good (VG)** condition. Holed or torn notes will be discounted.

1923 ISSUES

Denom.	Issue Date	Variety/Signature	VG Buying Price
25-cent	1923	Hyndman/Saunders	6.00
25-cent	1923	McCavour/Saunders	3.00
25-cent	1923	Campbell/Clark	3.00
$1	1923	Various Colour Seals	20.00
$1	1923	Purple Seal	55.00
$2	1923	Various Colour Seals	35.00
$2	1923	Green Seal	50.00
$2	1923	Bronze Seal	40.00

1924 AND 1925 ISSUES

Denom.	Issue Date	Variety/Signature	VG Buying Price
$5	1924	Queen Mary	2,500.00
$500	1925	George V	20,000.00
$1,000	1925	Queen Mary	22,500.00

Note: The buying prices listed are for notes in **Very Good (VG)** condition. Holed or torn notes will be discounted.

BANK OF CANADA

1935 ISSUES

Denom.	Variety	VG Buying Price
$1	English text	20.00
$1	French text	35.00
$2	English text	45.00
$2	French text	125.00
$5	English text	55.00
$5	French text	85.00
$10	English text	65.00
$10	French text	110.00
$20	English text	250.00

Denom.	Variety	VG Buying Price
$20	French text	500.00
$25	English text	1,500.00
$25	French text	1,750.00
$50	English text	900.00
$50	French text	1,350.00
$100	English text	750.00
$100	French text	1,300.00
$500	English or French	25,000.00
$1,000	English or French	2,100.00

Note: The buying prices listed are for notes in **Very Good (VG)** condition. Holed ot torn notes will be discounted.

1937 ISSUES

IMPORTANT

Denom.	Very Good Buying Prices By Signature		
	Osborne	Gordon	Coyne
$1	12.00	4.00	5.00
$2	25.00	9.00	9.00
$5	75.00	9.00	9.00
$10	40.00	11.00	11.00
$20	50.00	22.00	22.00
$50	200.00	55.00	55.00
$100	200.00	105.00	105.00
$1,000	1,700.00	NI	NI

IMPORTANT

The buying prices listed are for notes in **Very Good (VG)** condition. Notes of lower grades will be discounted.

- A. The note will have no tears, holes or writing of any kind and will be completely intact.
- B. Evidence of wear may be present along the edges and corners, with no weakness in the design. The corners will not be rounded.
- C. The note may have up to four major creases or folds with broken paper fibres, but no design loss in the creases.

Note: NI - Not issued

1954 ISSUES

"DEVIL'S FACE" PORTRAIT

THE DEVIL'S FACE NOTES

On the earliest notes of the 1954 issue, highlighted areas of the Queen's hair produced the illusion of a leering demonic face behind her ear. This was not the result of an error, nor was it, as some have asserted, the prank of an IRA sympathizer at the bank note company. It was merely the faithful reproduction of the original photograph. The portrait of the Queen with the devil's face outlined in her hair generated almost instant controversy.

ASTERISK NOTES

Asterisk notes are replacement notes, the first being spoiled in printing, cutting, etc., and replaced by an asterisk note. The asterisk is a small star-like symbol which appears before the prefix letters and serial number.

Denom.	Very Good Buying Price by Signature			
	Coyne/Towers		Beattie/Coyne	
	Regular	Asterisk	Regular	Asterisk
$1	7.00	400.00	5.00	300.00
$2	12.00	650.00	10.00	500.00
$5	15.00	2,100.00	12.00	1,100.00
$10	12.00	650.00	12.00	500.00
$20	17.00	1,000.00	15.00	2,400.00
$50	45.00	NI	50.00	NI
$100	60.00	NI	65.00	NI
$1,000	1,100.00	NI	NI	NI

IMPORTANT

The buying prices listed are for notes in **Very Good (VG)** condition.

Note:. NI - Not Issued

MODIFIED PORTRAIT

MODIFIED PORTRAIT

The portrait was modified by darkening the highlights in the hair and thus removing the shading which had resulted in the devil's face. The modification of the face plates was made for most denominations in 1956, except for the $1,000 denomination, which was modified several years later.

	Very Fine Buying Price by Signature							
	Beattie/Coyne		Beattie/Rasminsky		Bouey/Raminsky		Lawson/Bouey	
Denom.	Regular	Asterisk	Regular	Asterisk	Regular	Asterisk	Regular	Asterisk
$1	1.00	5.00	1.00	1.50	1.00	2.00	1.00	2.00
$2	2.00	15.00	2.00	3.00	2.00	3.00	2.00	3.00
$5	5.00	40.00	5.00	8.00	5.00	7.00	NI	NI
$10	10.00	60.00	10.00	15.00	NI	NI	NI	NI
$20	20.00	65.00	20.00	50.00	NI	NI	NI	NI
$50	50.00	NI	50.00	NI	NI	NI	50.00	NI
$100	100.00	NI	100.00	NI	NI	NI	100.00	NI
$1,000	1,025.00	NI	1,025.00	NI	1,025.00	NI	1,025.00	NI

IMPORTANT

The buying prices listed are for notes in **Very Fine (VF)** condition.

Note:. NI - Not Issued

$1 CENTENNIAL 1967

For the centennial of Canada's Confederation a special $1 note was issued. The note has a single design and two types of serial numbers, regular serial numbers and a special number "1867 - 1967." The special series was available from the Bank of Canada as a collector's item, but examples were soon found in circulation. In addition, there was an asterisk note series for replacement notes.

Denom.	Issue Date	Variety	Uncirculated Buying Price
$1	1967	Commemorative Serial Number 1867-1967	1.25
$1	1967	Regular Serial Number	1.50
$1	1967	Asterisk Serial Number	10.00

1969 - 1975 ISSUE

This new series combined fine line engraving with subtle variations to make notes that are extremely difficult to counterfeit. The series features a new portrait of the Queen, as well as portraits of previous prime ministers of Canada.

IMPORTANT

The buying prices listed on the following pages are for notes in **Uncirculated (Unc)** condition (new). The note must be clean, crisp, with no tears, creases, folds or marks of any kind or description.

ASTERISK AND "X" REPLACEMENT NOTES

Replacement of defective notes by asterisk notes was continued when the 1969-1975 issue was introduced. The highest denomination of the 1954 issue to be printed with asterisks was the $20; however, all denominations in the 1969-1975 issue, including the $50 and $100 notes, occur with asterisks in front of the two-letter prefix type.

When the triple-letter prefix notes were introduced in 1981, the use of the asterisk was discontinued. For triple-letter prefix notes, a replacement note was then designated by the use of an "X" for the third letter.

Asterisk Notes	"X" Replacement Notes
BC-46aA	BC-46A-i

	Uncirculated Buying Price by Signature									
	Beattie/ Rasminsky		Bouey/ Rasminsky		Lawson/Bouey			Crow/ Bouey		Thiessen/ Crow
Denom.	Regular	*	Regular	*	Regular	*	X	Regular	X	Regular	*
$1	NI	NI	NI	NI	1.	5.	10.	1.	5.	NI	NI
$2	NI	NI	NI	NI	3.	20.	50.	2.	75.	NI	NI
$5	NI	NI	10.	40.	10.	40.	NI	NI	NI	NI	NI
$10	20.	50.	20.	50.	15.	50.	400.	12.	40.	10.	30.
$20	30.	100.	NI	NI	25.	100.	NI	NI	NI	NI	NI
$50	NI	NI	NI	NI	60.	300.	1,000.	60.	100.	NI	NI
$100	NI	NI	NI	NI	100.	400.	750.	100.	125.	NI	NI

Note:
1. * Asterisk note
2. X Replacement note
3. NI Not issued

IMPORTANT

The buying prices listed on the following pages are for notes in **Uncirculated (Unc)** condition (new).

1979 ISSUES

The series beginning in 1979 is a modification of the previous issue. The face designs are similar, as is the colouration. The serial numbers are moved to the back of the note at the bottom, where the name of the Bank of Canada previously appeared. The black serial numbers are machine readable.

IMPORTANT

The buying prices listed below are for notes in uncirculated condition (new). The note must be clean, crisp, with no tears, creases, folds or marks of any kind or description.

REPLACEMENT NOTES

There are no asterisk notes in this issue. The replacement notes are designated by the second digit in the serial number.

The digit 1 following the first digit 3 of the $5 notes designates a replacement note. In the $20 denomination the replacement notes can be distinguished by "510" for the CBN company and "516" for the BABN company.

$5 Replacement Note $20 Replacement Note

	Uncirculated Buying Price by Signature					
	Lawson/Bouey		Crow/Bouey		Thiessen/Crow	
Denom.	Regular	Replace.	Regular	Replace.	Regular	Replace.
$5	10.00	200.00	10.00	300.00	NI	NI
$20	25.00	400.00	22.00	100.00	20.00	50.00

IMPORTANT

The buying prices listed on the following pages are for notes in **Uncirculated (Unc)** condition (new).

1986 BIRD ISSUES

On March 14, 1986, the Bank of Canada introduced a new series of bank notes. The new designs were launched that year with the issue of the $2 and $5 notes. The $1 and $2 bank notes have since been replaced with $1 and $2 coins.

FNX8282883

$5 Replacement Note. Prefix with an "X"

Denom.	Signature	Regular	Replacement
$2	Crow / Bouey	2.00	15.00
$5	Crow / Bouey	10.00	100.00

	Uncirculated Buying Price by Signature							
	Theissen/Crow		Bonin/Theissen		Knight/Thiessen		Knight/Dodge	
Denom.	Regular	Replace.	Regular	Replace.	Regular	Replace.	Regular	Replace.
$2	2.00	3.00	2.00	5.00	NI	NI	NI	NI
$5	10.00	25.00	5.00	100.00	5.00	100.00	5.00	15.00
$10	10.00	25.00	10.00	100.00	10.00	NI	NI	NI
$20	20.00	30.00	20.00	30.00	20.00	100.00	20.00	25.00
$50	50.00	100.00	50.00	NI	50.00	NI	50.00	75.00
$100	100.00	150.00	100.00	NI	100.00	NI	100.00	150.00
$1000	1,000.00	1,250.00	1,000.00	NI	NI	NI	NI	NI

IMPORTANT

1. The buying prices listed on the following pages are for notes in **Uncirculated (Unc)** condition (new).
2. Replacement notes have an X as the last letter of the prefix letters.

2001 JOURNEY ISSUES

Without Security Device

With Security Device

Without Security Device

With Security Device

Denom.		Uncirculated Buying Price by Signature		
	Knight/ Thiessen	Knight/ Dodge	Jenkins/ Dodge	Jenkins/ Carney	Macklem/ Carney
$5 Without Security Device	NI	5.00	5.00	NI	NI
$5 With Security Device	NI	NI	5.00	5.00	5.00
$10 Without Security Device	10.00	10.00	10.00	NI	NI
$10 With Security Device	NI	NI	10.00	10.00	10.00
$20 With Security Device	NI	NI	20.00	20.00	20.00
$50 With Security Device	NI	NI	50.00	50.00	50.00
$100 With Security Device	NI	NI	100.00	NI	NI

IMPORTANT

The buying prices listed on the following page are for notes in **Uncirculated (Unc)** condition (new).

Denom.	Description	Uncirculated Buying Price by Signature			
		Jenkins/ Dodge	Jenkins/ Carney	Macklem/ Carney	Poloz/ Wilkins
$5	Canadarm 2	—	—	—	5.00
$10	"The Canadian"	—	—	—	10.00
$20	Contributions	—	—	20.00	20.00
$50	Arctic Research	50.00	50.00	50.00	50.00
$100	Medical Innovation	100.00	100.00	100.00	100.00

NEWFOUNDLAND
PUBLIC WORKS CASH NOTES

1901-1909

Denom.	VG Buying Price
40 cents	300.00
50 cents	250.00
80 cents	250.00
$1	300.00
$5	1,000.00

1910-1911

Denom.	VG Buying Price
25 cents	100.00
50 cents	100.00
$1	200.00
$2	1,200.00
$5	2,000.00

GOVERNMENT NOTES

Denom.	VG Buying Price
$1	150.00
$2	250.00

PRINCE EDWARD ISLAND

Denom.	VG Buying Price
1848-1870 5s	1,000.00
1848-1870 10s	1,000.00
1848-1870 £1	1,000.00
1848-1870 £2	1,000.00
1848-1870 £5	1,000.00
1872 $10	2,000.00
1872 $20	2,000.00

NOVA SCOTIA

Denom.	VG Buying Price
1846-1854 £1	2,000.00
1861 $5	1,500.00

IMPORTANT

Prices given are for notes in VG or better condition.

CANADIAN COLONIAL TOKENS

Canada has produced a great number of tokens of various kinds over the years. Tokens were used as a form of currency prior to the institution of the decimal currency system in 1858 (Colonial issues are not all tokens, some being regal coins). After Confederation, other kinds of tokens appeared, such as those for services, transportation and advertising purposes.

NEWFOUNDLAND TOKENS

Date and Description	VG Buying Price
1858 Sailing Ship	375.00
1860 Fishery Rights	50.00

Date and Description	VG Buying Price
Rutherford - St. John's	5.00
Rutherford - Harbour Grace	4.00
McAuslane	2,750.00

Note: Buying prices quoted are for tokens in very good condition. Holed, bent or badly corroded tokens are worth substantially less.

Date and Description	VG Buying Price	Date and Description	VG Buying Price
Holey Dollar Ring*	3,500.00	McCarthy Penny	3,000.00
Holey Dollar Plug*	4,000.00	Sheaf of Wheat	1,000.00
McCausland Penny	1,500.00	Speed The Plough	4.00

Note: 1. Tokens must be in very good condition.
2. * Forgeries exist and are worth considerably less.

Date and Description	VG Buying Price	Date and Description	VG Buying Price
Fisheries & Agriculture	3.00	Fisheries & Agriculture	5.00
Self Government 1855 Prince Edward's	4.00	Ships Colonies 1815 One Penny	25.00
Self Government 1855 Prince Edward	3.00	Ships Colonies 1815 Publick Accommodation	25.00
Self Government 1857	3.00	Ships Colonies	4.00

Note: Tokens must be **VG (very good)** or better condition, with no discolouration or damage.

Date and Description	VG Buying Price	Date and Description	VG Buying Price
1823 Halfpenny	4.00	1840 Halfpenny	4.00
1824 Halfpenny	4.00	1840 Penny	4.00
1824 Penny	5.00	1843 Halfpenny	5.00
1832 Halfpenny	4.00	1843 Penny	5.00
1832 Penny	5.00	1856 Halfpenny	3.00
		1856 Penny	4.00

Date and Description	VG Buying Price	Date and Description	VG Buying Price
Broke - Halifax	6.00	Hosterman & Etter 1815	5.00
Convenience of Trade	30.00	Starr & Shannon	5.00
Carritt & Alport	9.00	Commercial Change	6.00
Hosterman & Etter, 1814	7.00	Miles W. White	7.00

Date and Description	VG Buying Price	Date and Description	VG Buying Price
John Alexr Barry	5.00	Trade & Navigation 1813	30.00
Halifax Nova Scotia	15.00	Trade & Navigation 1812 and 1813	4.00
W. A. & S. Black's	13.00	Pure Copper Preferable	4.00
J. Brown	6.00	Success to Navigation	4.00
W. L. White's	25.00	N.S & N.B. Success	15.00

Date and Description	VG Buying Price
1843 Halfpenny	3.00
1843 Penny	3.00
1854 Halfpenny	3.00
1854 Penny	3.00

Date and Description	VG Buying Price
McDermott	375.00
St. John	7.00
St. John's	6,000.00

LOWER CANADA TOKENS

Date and Description	VG Buying Price	Date and Description	VG Buying Price
Magdalen Island	35.00	Pro Bono Publico	5,000.00
Bank Token	3.00	Bank Token Halfpenny	3.00
Banque du Peuple, Maple Leaf	5.00	Bank Token Penny	3.00
Banque du Peuple, Wreath	5.00	Bank of Montreal, Sideview Halfpenny	750.00
		Bank of Montreal, Sideview Penny	750.00

Date and Description	VG Buying Price	Date and Description	VG Buying Price
Montreal Half Penny	5.00	Francis Mullins & Son	10.00
Canada Half Penny, 1841	5.00	R.W. Owen	6,000.00
For Public Accommodation	4.00	J. Shaw & Co.	6.00
T.S. Brown & Co.	4.00	J. Roy	40.00
Ths & Wm Molson	300.00	Agriculture & Commerce	3.00

Date and Description	VG Buying Price	Date and Description	VG Buying Price
Halfpenny Token 1812, Small Wreath	4.00	To Facilitate Trade	
Halfpenny Token 1812, Large Wreath	4.00	Military Bust 1825	4.00
Penny Token 1812	7.00	Civilian Bust 1825	1,000.00
Victoria Nobis Est	4.00	Spread Eagle	4.00
R H Half Penny	7.00	Halfpenny Token	5.00

LOWER CANADA TOKENS

Date and Description	VG Buying Price	Date and Description	VG Buying Price
Seated Justice	4.00	Commercial Change	5.00
Bust/Ships Colonies	6.00	Bust and Harp - 1820	15.00

WELLINGTON TOKENS

Date and Description	VG Buying Price	Date and Description	VG Buying Price
Field Marshal Wellington	4.00	The Illustrious Wellington	3.00
Marquis Wellington	7.00	Battle Token	3.00

Date and Description	VG Buying Price
Copper Company	500.00
Lesslie Halfpenny	6.00
Lesslie Twopenny	75.00
No Labour No Bread	5.00
Sir Isaac Brock	7.00

Date and Description	VG Buying Price
Success To Commerce	5.00
Upper & Lower Canada	35.00
Commercial Change 1815	35.00
Commerical Change 1820	4.00

Note: Not all Canadian colonial tokens are listed in this guide. For more detailed information see the Charlton Standard Catalogue of Canadian Colonial Tokens, 9th edition.

UPPER CANADA TOKENS

Date and Description	VG Buying Price	Date and Description	VG Buying Price
Commercial Change 1821		To Facilitate Trade	
Cask Marked Upper Canada	50.00	1823	7.00
Cask Marked Jamaica	1,000.00	1833	5.00
Province of Upper Canada	7.00	Commercial Change 1833	7.00

PROVINCE OF CANADA TOKENS

218

PROVINCE OF CANADA TOKENS

Date and Description	VG Buying Price
Bank of Montreal	
1842, 1844 Halfpenny	2.50
1845 Halfpenny	3,000.00
1837 Penny	100.00
1842 Penny	4.00

Date and Description	VG Buying Price
Quebec Bank, 1852 Halfpenny	2.50
Quebec Bank, 1852 Penny	4.00
Bank of Upper Canada 1850-1857	
Halfpenny	2.00
Penny	3.00

ANONYMOUS AND MISCELLANEOUS TOKENS

Date and Description	VG Buying Price
For General Accommodation	5.00
Success to Trade	25.00

Date and Description	VG Buying Price
Pure Copper Preferable	7.00
North American	12.00

BRITISH COLUMBIA TOKENS

Date and Description	VG Buying Price
1862 Pattern Gold $10	50,000.00
1862 Pattern Gold $20	50,000.00

NORTH WEST COMPANY

Date and Description	VG Buying Price
1820 North West Company Token	1,250.00

Note: Beware reproductions exist.

HUDSON'S BAY COMPANY

Date and Description	VG Buying Price
Hudson's Bay Company Tokens Set of four (1, ½, ¼, 1/8)	800.00

TRANSPORTATION TOKENS

Date and Description	VG Buying Price
Bridge Tokens, each	350.00
Montreal & Lachine Railroad	200.00
Montreal & Lachine Railroad Restrike Dated 1947	50.00

CANADIAN MEDALS

WAR MEDALS 1812 TO 1885

Army
Gold
Cross

Naval
General
Service
Medal

Army
Gold
Medal

Canadian
General
Service
Medal

Army
General
Service
Medal

Egyptian
Medal

Date and Description	Buying Price
Army Gold Cross	16,000.00
Army Gold Medal	6,000.00
Army General Service Medal 1812-1814	
Fort Detroit Bar	2,000.00
Chateauguay Bar	2,000.00
Chrysler's Farm Bar	2,000.00
Naval General Service Medal 1812-1814	200.00

Date and Description	Buying Price
Canadian General Service Medal	
Fenian Raid Bar 1866	200.00
Fenian Raid Bar 1870	200.00
Red River Bar 1870	550.00
Egypt Medal *	
The Nile Bar	550.00
Kirbekan Bar	550.00
* Awarded to Canadian Boatmen	

WAR MEDALS 1885 TO 1914

Khedive's
Bronze
Star

1914
Star

North West
Canada
Medal

1914-1915
Star

South
Africa
Medal

British
War
Medal

Date and Description	Buying Price
Khedive's Bronze Star	30.00
North West Canada Medal 1885	200.00
Saskatchewan Bar	250.00
Queen's South Africa	
1899-1900 on reverse	2,500.00
Dates removed	30.00
King's South Africa	30.00

Date and Description	Buying Price
1914 Star*	1,000.00
1914-1915 Star	8.00
British War Medal	20.00
Groups**	
Star, British War Medal (2)	45.00
Star, Allied Victory Medal	50.00
British War Medal (3)	

*Canadian Star awarded only to 2nd. Field Hospital.
**Groups to Canadian Veterans, both medals
named to same person

WAR MEDALS 1914 TO 1945

Allied
Victory
Medal

Canadian
Defence
Medal

Merchantile
Marine
War
Medal

Canadian
WW II
1939-1945
War
Medal

Canadian
Volunteer
Service
Medal

Atlantic
Air Crew
Europe
Africa
France and
Germany
Italy
Pacific
Burma

Date and Description	Buying Price	Date and Description	Buying Price
Allied Victory Medal	8.00	1939-1945 Star	7.00
Mercantile Marine War Medal	25.00	Atlantic Star	20.00
Canadian Volunteer Service Medal	17.00	Air Crew Europe	80.00
Defence Medal	16.00	Africa Star	7.00
1939-1945 War Medal	16.00	France and Germany Star	7.00
		Italy Star	7.00
		Pacific Star	12.00
		Burma Star	12.00

Note: The Canadian Volunteer Service Medal, the Canadian Defence Medal and the World War II Medal are issued in silver. Britain and other Commonwealth countries issued cupro-nickel medals.

WAR MEDALS
1951 TO 1973

COMMEMORATIVE MEDALS

Canadian
Korean
Medal

1911
Coronation
Medal

United
Nations
Korea
Medal

1935
Silver
Jubilee
Medal

United
Nations
Emergency
Medal

1937
Coronation
Medal

Date and Description	Buying Price
Canadian Korean War Medal, English	30.00
Canadian Korean War Medal, French	40.00
United Nations Korea Medal	15.00
United Nations Emergency Medal	15.00
United Nations Medal 1960 to present	15.00
International Commission Medal 1967	15.00
International Commission Medal 1973	12.00

Date and Description	Buying Price
King George V	
Coronation Medal - 1911	25.00
Silver Jubilee Medal - 1935	20.00
King George VI	
Coronation Medal - 1937	20.00

COMMEMORATIVE MEDALS

1953
Coronation
Medal

1977
Silver
Jubilee
Medal

1967
Canadian
Centennial
Medal

MEDALS FOR VALOUR AND SERVICE

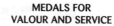

Victoria
Cross

Distinguished
Service
Order

Order of
St. Michael
and
St. George

Date and Description	Buying Price
Queen Elizabeth II	
Coronation Medal - 1953	25.00
Silver Jubilee Medal - 1977	40.00
Canadian Centennial Medal - 1967	40.00

Date and Description	Buying Price
Victoria Cross	40,000.00
Awarded to a Canadian	65,000.00
Distinguished Service Order	500.00
Order of St. Michael and St. George	250.00

Distinguished
Service
Cross

Air Force
Medal

Distinguished
Flying
Cross

Military
Medal

Air Force
Cross

British
Empire
Medal

Date and Description	Buying Price	Date and Description	Buying Price
Distinguished Service Cross	300.00	Air Force Medal	400.00
Distinguished Flying Cross	400.00	Military Medal	225.00
Air Force Cross	500.00	British Empire Medal	100.00

COINS OF THE UNITED STATES

MINT MARKS

The United States decimal coinage is identified by the following mint marks:

C	-Charlotte, North Carolina
CC	-Carson City, Nevada
D	-Dahlonega, Georgia (gold coins only)
D	-Denver, Colorado (1906 to date)
O	-New Orleans, Louisiana
S	-San Francisco, California
P	-Philadelphia, Pennsylvania

HALF CENTS

Liberty Cap

Date and Mint Mark	Buying Price
1793 Head Facing Left	1,000.00
1794	175.00
1795	130.00
1796	4,000.00
1797	150.00

Draped Bust

Date and Mint Mark	Buying Price
1800	25.00
1802	400.00
1803-1808	25.00

Classic Head

Date and Mint Mark	Buying Price
1809-1810	15.00
1811	200.00
1825 to 1829	15.00
1831 Proof only	1,000.00
1832 to 1835	14.00

Coronet Head

Date and Mint Mark	Buying Price
1849 to 1851	10.00
1852 Proof only	350.00
1853 to 1856	10.00
1857	20.00

IMPORTANT

Buying prices are for coins in VG condition. Coins in lessor grades such as Good or About Good will command lower buying prices.

LARGE CENTS

Flowing Hair

Date and Mint Mark	Buying Price
1793 Chain Reverse	3,000.00
1793 Wreath Reverse	1,000.00

Liberty Cap

Date and Mint Mark	Buying Price
1793	2,000.00
1794	150.00
1795	100.00
1796	125.00

Draped Bust

Date and Mint Mark	Buying Price
1796	100.00
1797	50.00
1798	30.00
1799	1,000.00
1800 to 1803	30.00
1804	300.00
1805 to 1807	25.00

Classic Head

Date and Mint Mark	Buying Price
1808	30.00
1809	60.00
1810	25.00
1811	40.00
1812 to 1814	25.00

Coronet Head

Date and Mint Mark	Buying Price
1816 to 1820	8.00
1821	15.00
1822	8.00
1823	30.00
1824 to 1838	7.00
1839 to 1856	7.00
1857	20.00

SMALL CENTS

Flying Eagle

Date and Mint Mark	Buying Price
1856*	3,000.00
1857 to 1858	8.00

* Counterfeits exist

Indian Head

Date and Mint Mark	Buying Price
1859	5.00
1860 to 1864	4.00
1865 to 1868	14.00
1869 to 1872	25.00
1873 to 1876	8.00
1877	300.00
1878	10.00
1879 to 1886	1.00
1887 to 1908	.25
1908S	25.00
1909	4.00
1909S	20.00

Lincoln Head Wheat Ears

Date and Mint Mark	Buying Price
19091	.50
1909VDB	4.00
1909S	25.00
1909S VDB	200.00
1910 to 1914	.05
1914D	70.00
1915D to 1931D	.02
1931S	30.00
1932 to 1958	.01
1955 Double Die	100.00

Lincoln Head Memorial

Date and Mint Mark	Buying Price
1959 to 2008	.01

TWO CENTS

Date and Mint Mark	Buying Price
1864 to 1871	5.00
1872	150.00
1873 Proofs only	500.00

THREE CENTS

Silver

Date and Mint Mark	Buying Price
1851 to 1862	8.00
1863 to 1872	100.00
1873 Proofs only	300.00

Nickel

Date and Mint Mark	Buying Price
1865 to 1874	5.00
1875 to 1876	8.00
1877 to 1878 Proofs only	300.00
1879 to 1880	25.00
1881	5.00
1882	25.00
1883	50.00
1884 to 1887	120.00
1888	20.00
1889	25.00

HALF DIMES

Flowing Hair

Date and Mint Mark	Buying Price
1794	500.00
1795	400.00

Draped Bust

Date and Mint Mark	Buying Price
1796 to 1797	500.00
1800 to 1801	300.00
1802	10,000.00
1803 to 1805	300.00

Capped Bust

Date and Mint Mark	Buying Price
1829 to 1837	25.00

Liberty Seated

Date and Mint Mark	Buying Price
1837 Large Date	15.00
1837 Small Date	15.00
1838 to 1845	5.00
1838 O	30.00

Date and Mint Mark	Buying Price
1844O	20.00
1846	100.00
1847 to 1862	5.00
1863	50.00
1863S	10.00
1864	100.00
1864S	10.00
1865	60.00
1865S	10.00
1866	60.00
1866S	10.00
1867	150.00
1867S to 1873S	5.00

FIVE CENTS NICKEL

Shield

Date and Mint Mark	Buying Price
1866 to 1870	5.00
1871	20.00
1872 to 1876	10.00
1877 and 1878 Proofs only	500.00
1879 to 1881	100.00
1882 to 1883	5.00

Liberty Head

Date and Mint Mark	Buying Price
1883	2.00
1884	5.00
1885	200.00
1886	100.00
1887 to 1898	2.00
1899 to 1912D	.25
1912S	50.00

Indian Head

Date and Mint Mark	Buying Price
1913 and 1913D	3.00
1913S	15.00
1914D	25.00
1914S	10.00
1914 to 1918	1.00
1918D 8/7	500.00
1919 to 1938	.20

Jefferson Head

Date and Mint Mark	Buying Price
1938 to 1942 Nickel	.05
1942 to 1945 Silver, Large P, D, or S above Monticello	.25
1946 to 2003 Nickel	.05

DIMES

Draped Bust

Date and Mint Mark	Buying Price
1796 to 1797	750.00
1798 to 1807	200.00

Capped Bust

Date and Mint Mark	Buying Price
1809 to 1811	50.00
1814 to 1821	10.00
1822	200.00
1823 to 1837	10.00

Liberty Seated

Date and Mint Mark	Buying Price
1837 and 1838O No stars	12.00
1838 to 1840O Stars	5.00
1841 to 1843	5.00
1843O	20.00
1844	100.00
1845 to 1845O	5.00
1846	40.00
1847 to 1856	4.00
1856S	65.00
1857 to 1860	4.00
1858S	40.00
1859S	50.00
1860O	150.00
1861 to 1862	4.00
1863	100.00
1863S	10.00
1864	50.00
1864S	10.00
1865	100.00
1865S	10.00
1866	125.00
1866S	10.00
1867	150.00
1867S	10.00
1868 to 1874	5.00
1871CC	750.00
1872CC	250.00
1873CC Arrows	600.00
1874CC Arrows	1,000.00
1875 to 1878	4.00
1878CC	20.00
1879 to 1881	60.00
1882 to 1885	4.00
1885S	150.00
1886 to 1891	3.50

Barber

Date and Mint Mark	Buying Price
1892 to 1895	4.00
1895O	125.00
1896O and S	40.00
1897 to 1916	1.00

Mercury Head

Date and Mint Mark	Buying Price
1916	1.20
1916D	500.00
1917 to 1945	1.20
1921	22.00
1921D	40.00

Roosevelt - Silver

Date and Mint Mark	Buying Price
1946 to 1964	1.00

Roosevelt - Clad

Date and Mint Mark	Buying Price
1965 to 2014	.10

TWENTY CENTS

Date and Mint Mark	Buying Price
1875 to 1876	50.00
1875CC	100.00
1876CC	10,000.00
1877 to 1878 Proofs only	700.00

QUARTER DOLLAR

Draped Bust

Date and Mint Mark	Buying Price
1796	4,000.00
1804	2,000.00
1805 to 1807	200.00

Capped Bust

Date and Mint Mark	Buying Price
1815 to 1822	40.00
1823/2	5,000.00
1824 to 1828	40.00
1831 to 1838 Reduced Size	25.00

Liberty Seated

Date and Mint Mark	Buying Price
1838 to 1841	10.00
1842 Large Date	25.00
1842O Small Date	125.00
1842O Large date	10.00
1843 to 1849	8.00
1849O	200.00
1850 to 1851	10.00
1851O	60.00
1852	15.00
1852O	60.00
1853 to 1865	8.00
1862S and 1865S	20.00
1864S	100.00
1866 to 1867S	75.00
1868 to 1870	25.00
1870CC and 1871CC	1,000.00
1871 to 1878CC	10.00
1871S	100.00
1872CC	300.00
1872S	250.00
1873CC	2,000.00
1878S to 1888	50.00
1888S	8.00
1889 and 1890	20.00
1891 and 1891S	8.00
1891O	60.00

Barber

Date and Mint Mark	Buying Price
1892 to 1896	6.00
1896S	300.00
1897 to 1901	3.00
1901S	2,500.00
1902 to 1913	3.00
1913S	600.00
1914 to 1916D	2.75

Standing Liberty

Date and Mint Mark	Buying Price
1916	2,000.00
1917 to 1924	8.00
1923S	125.00
1925 to 1930	2.75

Washington - Silver

Date and Mint Mark	Buying Price
1932 to 1964	2.50
1927S	20.00
1932D	50.00
1932S	50.00
1933 to 1964	2.50

Washington - Clad

Date and Mint Mark	Buying Price
1965 to 1998	.25

200th Bi-Centennial

Date and Mint Mark	Buying Price
1976	.25

STATE QUARTERS

Delaware

Pennsylvania

Maryland

South Carolina

New Jersey

Georgia

New Hampshire

Virginia

Connecticut

Massachusetts

New York

North Carolina

Date and Mint Mark	Description	Buying Price	Date and Mint Mark	Description	Buying Price
1999P	Delaware, MS	.25	2000P	Maryland, MS	.25
1999D	Delaware, MS	.25	2000D	Maryland, MS	.25
1999S	Delaware, PR	1.25	2000S	Maryland, PR	1.25
1998S	Delaware, Silver	5.00	2000S	Maryland, Silver	5.00
1999P	Pennsylvania, MS	.25	2000P	South Carolina, MS	.25
1999D	Pennsylvania, MS	.25	2000D	South Carolina, MS	.25
1999S	Pennsylvania, PR	1.25	2000S	South Carolina, PR	1.25
1999S	Pennsylvania, Silver	5.00	2000S	South Carolina, Silver	5.00
1999P	New Jersey, MS	.25	2000P	New Hampshire, MS	.25
1999D	New Jersey, MS	.25	2000D	New Hampshire, MS	.25
1999S	New Jersey, PR	1.25	2000S	New Hampshire, PR	1.25
1999S	New Jersey, Silver	5.00	2000S	New Hampshire, Silver	5.00
1999P	Georgia, MS	.25	2000P	Virginia, MS	.25
1999D	Georgia, MS	.25	2000D	Virginia, MS	.25
1999S	Georgia, PR	1.25	2000S	Virginia, PR	1.25
1999S	Georgia, Silver	5.00	2000S	Virginia, Silver	5.00
1999P	Connecticut, MS	.25	2001P	New York, MS	.25
1999D	Connecticut, MS	.25	2001D	New York, MS	.25
1999S	Connecticut, PR	1.25	2001S	New York, PR	1.25
1999S	Connecticut, Silver	5.00	2001S	New York, Silver	5.00
2000P	Massachusetts, MS	.25	2001P	North Carolina, MS	.25
2000D	Massachusetts, MS	.25	2001D	North Carolina, MS	.25
2000S	Massachusetts, PR	1.25	2001S	North Carolina, PR	1.25
2000S	Massachusetts, Silver	5.00	2001S	North Carolina, Silver	5.00

| Rhode Island | Vermont | Indiana | Mississippi |

| Kentucky | Tennessee | Illinois | Alabama |

| Ohio | Louisiana | Maine | Missouri |

Date and Mint Mark	Description	Buying Price	Date and Mint Mark	Description	Buying Price
2001P	Rhode Island, MS	.25	2002P	Indiana, MS	.25
2001D	Rhode Island, MS	.25	2002D	Indiana, MS	.25
2001S	Rhode Island, PR	1.25	2002S	Indiana, PR	1.25
2001S	Rhode Island, Silver	5.00	2002S	Indiana, Silver	5.00
2001P	Vermont, MS	.25	2002P	Mississippi, MS	.25
2001D	Vermont, MS	.25	2002D	Mississippi, MS	.25
2001S	Vermont, PR	1.25	2002S	Mississippi, PR	1.25
2001S	Vermont, Silver	5.00	2002S	Mississippi, Silver	5.00
2001P	Kentucky, MS	.25	2003P	Illinois, MS	.25
2001D	Kentucky, MS	.25	2003D	Illinois, MS	.25
2001S	Kentucky, PR	1.25	2003S	Illinois, PR	1.25
2001S	Kentucky, Silver	5.00	2003S	Illinois, Silver	5.00
2002P	Tennessee, MS	.25	2003P	Alabama, MS	.25
2002D	Tennessee, MS	.25	2003D	Alabama, MS	.25
2002S	Tennessee, PR	1.25	2003S	Alabama, PR	1.25
2002S	Tennessee, Silver	5.00	2003S	Alabama, Silver	5.00
2002P	Ohio, MS	.25	2003P	Maine, MS	.25
2002D	Ohio, MS	.25	2003D	Maine, MS	.25
2002S	Ohio, PR	1.25	2003S	Maine, PR	1.25
2002S	Ohio, Silver	5.00	2003S	Maine, Silver	5.00
2002P	Louisiana, MS	.25	2003P	Missouri, MS	.25
2002D	Louisiana, MS	.25	2003D	Missouri, MS	.25
2002S	Louisiana, PR	1.25	2003S	Missouri, PR	1.25
2002S	Louisiana, Silver	5.00	2003S	Missouri, Silver	5.00

Arkansas	Michigan	California	Minnesota
Florida	Texas	Oregon	Kansas
Iowa	Wisconsin	West Virginia	Nevada

Date and Mint Mark	Description	Buying Price	Date and Mint Mark	Description	Buying Price
2003P	Arkansas, MS	.25	2005P	California, MS	.25
2003D	Arkansas, MS	.25	2005D	California, MS	.25
2003S	Arkansas, PR	1.25	2005S	California, PR	1.25
2003S	Arkansas, Silver	5.00	2005S	California, Silver	5.00
2004P	Michigan, MS	.25	2005P	Minnesota, MS	.25
2004D	Michigan, MS	.25	2005D	Minnesota, MS	.25
2004S	Michigan, PR	1.25	2005S	Minnesota, PR	1.25
2004S	Michigan, Silver	5.00	2005S	Minnesota, Silver	5.00
2004P	Florida, MS	.25	2005P	Oregon, MS	.25
2004D	Florida, MS	.25	2005D	Oregon, MS	.25
2004S	Florida, PR	1.25	2005S	Oregon, PR	1.25
2004S	Florida, Silver	5.00	2005S	Oregon, Silver	5.00
2004P	Texas, MS	.25	2005P	Kansas, MS	.25
2004D	Texas, MS	.25	2005D	Kansas, MS	.25
2004S	Texas, PR	1.25	2005S	Kansas, PR	1.25
2004S	Texas, Silver	5.00	2005S	Kansas, Silver	5.00
2004P	Iowa, MS	.25	2005P	West Virginia, MS	.25
2004D	Iowa, MS	.25	2005D	West Virginia, MS	.25
2004S	Iowa, PR	1.25	2005S	West Virginia, PR	1.25
2004S	Iowa, Silver	5.00	2005S	West Virginia, Silver	5.00
2004P	Wisconsin, MS	.25	2006P	Nevada, MS	.25
2004D	Wisconsin, MS	.25	2006D	Nevada, MS	.25
2004S	Wisconsin, PR	1.25	2006S	Nevada, PR	2.00
2004S	Wisconsin, Silver	5.00	2006S	Nevada, Silver	5.00

STATE QUARTERS (cont.)

Nebraska   Colorado   Idaho   Wyoming

North Dakota   South Dakota   Utah   Oklahoma

Montana   Washington   New Mexico   Arizona

Date and Mint Mark	Description	Buying Price
2006P	Nebraska, MS	.25
2006D	Nebraska, MS	.25
2006S	Nebraska, PR	1.25
2006S	Nebraska, Silver	5.00
2006P	Colorado, MS	.25
2006D	Colorado, MS	.25
2006S	Colorado, PR	1.25
2006S	Colorado, Silver	5.00
2006P	North Dakota, MS	.25
2006D	North Dakota, MS	.25
2006S	North Dakota, PR	1.25
2006S	North Dakota, Silver	5.00
2006P	South Dakota, MS	.25
2006D	South Dakota, MS	.25
2006S	South Dakota, PR	1.25
2006S	South Dakota, Silver	5.00
2007P	Montana, MS	.25
2007D	Montana, MS	.25
2007S	Montana, PR	1.25
2007S	Montana, Silver	5.00
2007P	Washington, MS	.25
2007D	Washington, MS	.25
2007S	Washington, PR	1.25
2007S	Washington, Silver	5.00

Date and Mint Mark	Description	Buying Price
2007P	Idaho, MS	.25
2007D	Idaho, MS	.25
2007S	Idaho, PR	1.25
2007S	Idaho, Silver	5.00
2007P	Wyoming, MS	.25
2007D	Wyoming, MS	.25
2007S	Wyoming, PR	1.25
2007S	Wyoming, Silver	5.00
2007P	Utah, MS	.25
2007D	Utah, MS	.25
2007S	Utah, PR	1.25
2007S	Utah, Silver	5.00
2008P	Oklahoma, MS	.25
2008D	Oklahoma, MS	.25
2008S	Oklahoma, PR	1.25
2008S	Oklahoma, Silver	5.00
2008P	New Mexico, MS	.25
2008D	New Mexico, MS	.25
2008S	New Mexico, PR	1.25
2008S	New Mexico, Silver	5.00
2008P	Arizona, MS	.25
2008D	Arizona, MS	.25
2008S	Arizona, PR	1.25
2008S	Arizona, Silver	5.00

STATE QUARTERS (cont.)

Alaska

Hawaii

District of Columbia

Puerto Rico

Guam

American Samoa

U.S. Virgin Islands

Northern Mariana Islands

Date and Mint Mark	Description	Buying Price
2008P	Alaska, MS	.25
2008D	Alaska, MS	.25
2008S	Alaska, PR	1.25
2008S	Alaska, Silver	5.00
2008P	Hawaii, MS	.25
2008D	Hawaii, MS	.25
2008S	Hawaii, PR	1.25
2008S	Hawaii, Silver	5.00
2009P	District of Columbia, MS	.25
2009D	District of Columbia, MS	.25
2009S	District of Columbia, PR	1.25
2009S	District of Columbia, Silver	5.00
2009P	Puerto Rico, MS	.25
2009D	Puerto Rico, MS	.25
2009S	Puerto Rico, PR	1.25
2009S	Puerto Rico, Silver	5.00

Date and Mint Mark	Description	Buying Price
2009P	Guam, MS	.25
2009D	Guam, MS	.25
2009S	Guam, PR	1.25
2009S	Guam, Silver	5.00
2009P	American Samoa, MS	.25
2009D	American Samoa, MS	.25
2009S	American Samoa, PR	1.25
2009S	American Samoa, Silver	5.00
2009P	U.S. Virgin Islands, MS	.25
2009D	U.S. Virgin Islands, MS	.25
2009S	U.S. Virgin Islands, PR	1.25
2009S	U.S. Virgin Islands, Silver	5.00
2009P	Northern Mariana Islands, MS	.25
2009D	Northern Mariana Islands, MS	.25
2009S	Northern Mariana Islands, PR	1.25
2009S	Northern Mariana Islands, Silver	5.00

AMERICA THE BEAUTIFUL
2010-2021

Date and Mint Mark	Description	Buying Price
2010P	Hot Springs MS	.25
2010P	Yellowstone, MS	.25
2010P	Yosemite, MS	.25
2010P	Grand Canyon, MS	.25
2010P	Mount Hood, MS	.25
2011P	Gettysburg, MS	.25
2011P	Glacier, MS	.25
2011P	Olympic, MS	.25

Date and Mint Mark	Description	Buying Price
2011P	Vicksburg, MS	.25
2011P	Chickasaw, MS	.25
2012P	El Yunque	.25
2012P	Chaco Culture	.25
2012P	Acadia	.25
2012P	Hawi'i Volcanoes	.25
2012P	Denali	.25

Note: MS is **Mint State**, uncirculated business strike.
PR is **Proof Condition**, collector coins of high quality mirror finish.
Silver Proofs are .900 fine silver coins with a high quality mirror finish.

HALF DOLLARS
Flowing Hair

Date and Mint Mark	Buying Price
1794	2,000.00
1795	300.00

Draped Bust

Date and Mint Mark	Buying Price
1796 15 Stars	10,000.00
1796 16 Stars	10,000.00
1797 15 Stars	10,000.00
1801 to 1802	300.00
1803 to 1807	75.00

Capped Bust

Date and Mint Mark	Buying Price
1807	60.00
1808 to 1814	25.00
1815	500.00

Date and Mint Mark	Buying Price
1817 to 1836	25.00
1837 to 1839	25.00
1839O	75.00

Liberty Seated

Date and Mint Mark	Buying Price
1839 to 1852O	20.00
1850	75.00
1851	100.00
1852	125.00
1853O No Arrows	25,000.00
1853 to 1855	15.00
1855S Arrows	125.00
1856 to 1865S	12.00
1866 to 1873CC	12.00
1870CC	500.00
1871CC	100.00
1873 to 1874S	15.00
1875 to 1878	15.00
1878CC	300.00
1878S	7,500.00
1879 to 1890	75.00
1891	15.00

Barber

Date and Mint Mark	Buying Price
1892	5.50
1892O	100.00
1892S	75.00
1893 to 1897	5.50
1893S	50.00
1897O	50.00
1897S	35.00
1898 to 1915	5.50

Liberty Walking

Date and Mint Mark	Buying Price
1916 to 1920	5.00
1921	60.00
1921D	100.00
1923 to 1947	5.00

Franklin

Date and Mint Mark	Buying Price
1948 to 1964	5.00

Kennedy - Silver

Date and Mint Mark	Buying Price
1964	5.00

Kennedy - Silver Clad

Date and Mint Mark	Buying Price
1965 to 1970	2.25

Kennedy - Copper Clad

Date and Mint Mark	Buying Price
1971 to 2014	.50

SILVER DOLLARS

Flowing Hair

Date and Mint Mark	Buying Price
1794	20,000.00
1795	600.00

Draped Bust

Date and Mint Mark	Buying Price
1795	500.00
1796 to 1798	450.00
1798 to 1803	275.00

Note: Silver dollars must grade very good (VG) or better to command prices listed.

Liberty Seated

Peace

Date and Mint Mark	Buying Price
1840 to 1873	75.00
1851 and 1852	2,000.00
1854	450.00
1855	300.00
1858 Proofs only	1,000.00
1870CC	125.00
1870S	20,000.00
1871CC	1,000.00
1872CC	400.00
1872S	100.00
1873CC	1,300.00

Date and Mint Mark	Buying Price
1921	35.00
1922 to 1927	15.00
1928	125.00
1928S to 1935S	15.00

Eisenhower

Liberty Head

Date and Mint Mark	Buying Price
1971 to 1978	1.00

Susan B. Anthony

Date and Mint Mark	Buying Price
1878 to 1892	15.00
1878CC to 1881CC	35.00
1882CC to 1884CC	30.00
1885CC	125.00
1889CC	350.00
1893CC	100.00
1890O to 1893O	15.00
1893S	1,100.00
1894	450.00
1895	6,500.00
1895O	100.00
1895S	150.00
1896 to 1903	15.00
1903O	100.00
1904 to 1921	15.00

Date and Mint Mark	Buying Price
1979 P.D & S	1.00
1980 P.D & S	1.00
1981 P.D & S	1.00
1999 P & D	1.00

TRADE DOLLARS

Date and Mint Mark	Buying Price
1873 to 1878	50.00
1878CC	150.00
1879 to 1883	300.00

GOLD DOLLARS

Type 1 Liberty Head

Date and Mint Mark	Buying Price
1849 to 1854	140.00
1849C	350.00
1849D	450.00
1850C	350.00
1850D	450.00
1851C	400.00
1851D	425.00
1852C	350.00
1852D	475.00

Type 2 Indian Head, Small

Date and Mint Mark	Buying Price
1854 to 1855	250.00
1855C	450.00
1855D	1,600.00
1855O	250.00
1856S	300.00

GOLD DOLLARS
Type 3 Indian Head, Large

Date and Mint Mark	Buying Price
1856 to 1889	150.00
1856D	1,100.00
1860D	840.00
1861D	2,000.00
1875	700.00

GOLD 2 ½ DOLLARS
Capped Bust Right

Date and Mint Mark	Buying Price
1796	6,000.00
1797 to 1807	1,500.00

Capped Bust Left

Date and Mint Mark	Buying Price
1808	6,000.00

Capped Head Left

Date and Mint Mark	Buying Price
1821 to 1827	1,500.00
1829 to 1833	1,700.00
1834 No Motto	3,000.00

Classic Head

Date and Mint Mark	Buying Price
1834 to 1839	225.00

Coronet Head

Date and Mint Mark	Buying Price
1840 to 1907	160.00
1848 California	6,000.00
1854D	1,000.00
1854S	15,000.00
1855D	1,000.00
1856D	2,500.00
1875	1,500.00

Indian Head

Date and Mint Mark	Buying Price
1908 to 1929	160.00
1911D	900.00

GOLD 3 DOLLARS

Date and Mint Mark	Buying Price
1854 to 1873	500.00
1854D	4,000.00
1873 Closed 3	1,400.00
1880 to 1889	450.00

GOLD 4 DOLLARS

Date and Mint Mark	Buying Price
1879 to 1880	25,000.00

GOLD 5 DOLLARS

Capped Bust - Small Eagle

Date and Mint Mark	Buying Price
1795 to 1797	4,500.00
1798	20,000.00

Capped Bust - Heraldic Eagle

Date and Mint Mark	Buying Price
1795 to 1797	2,000.00
1798 to 1807	1,000.00

IMPORTANT: Buying prices listed are for gold coins graded VF or better. Bent, damaged or badly worn coins are worth bullion value.

Capped Draped Bust Left

Date and Mint Mark	Buying Price
1807 to 1812	1,000.00

Capped Head

Date and Mint Mark	Buying Price
1813 to 1820	1,500.00
1815	20,000.00
1819	3,000.00
1821	3,000.00
1823	1,500.00
1824 to 1826	2,000.00
1829	8,000.00
1830 to 1834	5,000.00

Classic Head

Date and Mint Mark	Buying Price
1834 to 1838	325.00
1838C	1,000.00
1838D	1,000.00

Coronet Head

Date and Mint Mark	Buying Price
1839 to 1908	315.00
1842C Large Date	400.00
1842C Small Date	1,500.00
1854S	35,000.00
1861C	600.00
1861D	1,500.00
1864S	1,600.00
1865S	400.00
1866S	450.00
1870CC	1,800.00
1875	8,000.00
1878CC	850.00

Indian Head

Date and Mint Mark	Buying Price
1908 to 1916	300.00
1909O	750.00
1929	2,000.00

GOLD 10 DOLLARS
Capped Bust Right

Date and Mint Mark	Buying Price
Small Eagle, 1795 to 1797	6,000.00
Heraldic Eagle, 1797 to 1804	2,250.00

Coronet Head

Date and Mint Mark	Buying Price
1838 to 1907S	625.00
1858	1,500.00
1859O	1,500.00
1859S	725.00
1863	1,200.00
1864S	1,500.00
1865S	1,000.00
1866S	600.00
1867S	600.00
1870CC	2,500.00
1871CC	750.00
1872	800.00
1872CC	750.00
1873	1,500.00
1873CC	1,100.00
1875	15,000.00
1875CC	1,100.00
1876	950.00
1876CC	1,000.00
1877	800.00
1877CC	800.00
1878CC	1,000.00
1879CC	1,750.00
1879O	725.00
1883O	900.00

GOLD $20 DOLLARS
Liberty

Date and Mint Mark	Buying Price
1850 to 1907S	1,250.00
1854O	20,000.00
1855O	3,000.00
1856O	25,000.00
1859O	4,000.00
1860O	4,000.00
1861O	4,000.00
1866S	1,275.00
1870CC	35,000.00
1871CC	2,000.00
1872CC	1,275.00
1879O	4,000.00
1881	3,000.00
1882	4,000.00
1885	2,500.00
1886	5,000.00
1891	1,750.00
1891CC	1,750.00

$20 St. Gaudens

$10 Indian Head

Date and Mint Mark	Buying Price
1907 to 1932	625.00
1920S	2,500.00
1930S	2,000.00
1933	20,000.00

Date and Mint Mark	Buying Price
1907 MCMVII	3,000.00
1907 to 1916	1,250.00
1920S	7,000.00
1921	8,000.00
1922 to 1928	1,275.00
1927D	50,000.00
1927S	5,000.00
1929	6,000.00
1930 to 1932	5,000.00

GOLD COMMEMORATIVE COINS

Date and Mint Mark	Buying Price	Date and Mint Mark	Buying Price
1903 $1 Louisiana Purchase	275.00	1995W $5 Olympic Torch (MS)	300.00
1904-05 $1 Lewis & Clark Exposition	400.00	1195W $5 Olympic Torch (PR)	300.00
1915S $1 Panama-Pacific Exposition	275.00	1995W $5 Olympic Stadium (MS)	400.00
1916 $1 McKinley Memorial	275.00	1995W $5 Olympic Stadium (PR)	400.00
1917 $1 McKinley Memorial	325.00	1996W $5 Olympic Flag Bearer (MS)	475.00
1922 $1 Grant Memorial, With Star	700.00	1996W $5 Olympic Flag Bearer (PR)	475.00
1922 $1 Grant Memorial, Without Star	700.00	1996W $5 Olympic Cauldron (MS)	300.00
1915S $2.50 Panama-Pacific Exposition	750.00	1996W $5 Olympic Cauldron (PR)	300.00
1926 $2.50 Philadelphia Sesquicentennial	175.00	1996W $5 Smithsonian	385.00
1984P and D $10 Olympic	600.00	1997W $5 F.D.R.	325.00
1984S $10 Olympic	600.00	1997W $5 Jackie Robinson	500.00
1984W $10 Olympic	600.00	1999W $5 George Washington	300.00
1986W $5 Liberty	300.00	2000W $10 Library of Congress	600.00
1987W $5 Constitution	300.00	2001W $5 Capitol Visitor Centre	300.00
1988W $5 Oylmpic	300.00	2002W $5 Salt Lake City Olympics	300.00
1989W $5 Congress	300.00	2003W $10 First Flight	450.00
1991W $5 Mount Rushmore	300.00	2006S $5 San Francisco Mint Museum	300.00
1992W $5 Olympic	300.00	2007W $5 Jamestown	300.00
1992W $5 Columbus	300.00	2008W $5 Bald Eagle	300.00
1993W $5 Bill of Rights	300.00	2011P&S $5 United States Army	300.00
1994W $5 World Cup	300.00	2011P $5 Medal of Honor	300.00
1995W $5 Civil War	350.00	2012W $5 Star-Spangled Banner	300.00
1995W $5 WWII	300.00	2013P&S $5 Five Star Generals	300.00

SILVER COMMEMORATIVE COINS

Date and Mint Mark	Buying Price	Date and Mint Mark	Buying Price
1982D or S 50¢ George Washington	6.00	1996D $1 Olympics, High Jump (MS)	150.00
1983P, D or S $1 Los Angeles Olympics	13.00	1996P $1 Olympics, High Jump (PR)	15.00
1984P, D or S, $1 Los Angeles Olympics	13.00	1996D $1 Paralympics (MS)	150.00
1986D or S 50¢ Statue of Liberty	6.00	1996P $1 Paralympics (PR)	35.00
1986P or S $1 Statue of Liberty	13.00	1996D $1 Olympics, Rowing (MS)	150.00
1987P or S $1 Constitution	13.00	1996P $1 Olympics, Rowing (PR)	15.00
1988D or S $1 Seoul Olympiad	13.00	1996D $1 Olympics, Tennis (MS)	150.00
1989D or S 50¢ Congress	6.00	1996P $1 Olympics, Tennis (PR)	35.00
1989D or S $1 Congress	13.00	1996D $1 Smithsonian (MS)	65.00
1990W or P $1 Eisenhower	13.00	1996P $1 Smithsonian (PR)	15.00
1991D or P $1 Korean War	13.00	1996S $1 Community Service (MS)	100.00
1991D or S 50¢ Mount Rushmore	6.00	1996S $1 Community Service (PR)	35.00
1991D or S $1 USO	13.00	1997P $1 Botanic Gardens (MS & PR)	15.00
1991P or S $1 Mount Rushmore	13.00	1997P $1 Law Enforcement (MS & PR)	60.00
1992D or W $1 White House	13.00	1997S $1 Robinson (MS & PR)	40.00
1992D or S $1 XXV Olympiad	13.00	1998S $1 Black Patriots (MS & PR)	50.00
1992P or S 50¢ XXV Olympiad	6.00	1998S $1 Robert F. Kennedy (MS & PR)	15.00
1992D or S 50¢ Christopher Columbus	6.00	1999P $1 Dolly Madison (MS & PR)	15.00
1992D or P $1 Christopher Columbus	13.00	1999P $1 Yellowstone (MS & PR)	15.00
1993D or W $1 D-Day	13.00	2000P $1 Leif Ericson (MS & PR)	40.00
1993-1994P or S $1 Thomas Jefferson	13.00	2000P $1 Library of Congress (MS & PR)	15.00
1993W or S 50¢ Bill of Rights	6.00	2001P or D $1 American Indian	150.00
1993W or S $1 Bill of Rights	13.00	2001P 50¢ U.S. Capitol (MS & PR)	6.00
1994D or P 50¢ World Cup	6.00	2002P $1 Olympics, Salt Lake City (MS & PR)	15.00
1994D or S $1 World Cup	13.00	2002W $1 West Point	15.00
1994D or S $1 U.S. Capitol	13.00	2003P 50¢ First Flight (MS & PR)	6.00
1994W or P $1 Vietnam Veterans Mem.	45.00	2003P $1 First Flight (MS & PR)	15.00
1994W or P $1 U.S. Prisoner of War Museum	50.00	2004P $1 Edison (MS & PR)	15.00
1994W or P $1 Women in Military	13.00	2004P $1 Lewis & Clark (MS & PR)	15.00
1995P 50¢ 50th Anniversary WWII	6.00	2005P $1 Chief Justice J. Marshall (MS & PR)	15.00
1995S 50¢ Civil War Battlefields	13.00	2005P $1 U.S. Marine Corps (MS & PR)	15.00
1995P or S $1 Civil War Battlefields	20.00	2006P $1 Benjamin Franklin, Signature	15.00
1995S 50¢ Olympics, Baseball (MS)	6.00	2006P $1 Benjamin Franklin, Kite	15.00
1995S 50¢ Olympics, Baseball (PR)	6.00	2006S $1 San Francisco Mint Museum	15.00
1995S 50¢ Olympics, Basketball (MS)	6.00	2007P $1 Jamestown, 400th (MS & PR)	15.00
1995S 50¢ Olympics, Basketball (PR)	6.00	2007P $1 Little Rock High School	15.00
1995D $1 Olympics, Cycling (MS)	60.00	2008S $1 Bald Eagle (MS & PR)	15.00
1995P $1 Olympics, Cycling (PR)	13.00	2008S 50¢ Bald Eagle (MS & PR)	15.00
1995D $1 Olympics, Gymnastics (MS)	20.00	2009P $1 Louis Braille (MS & PR)	15.00
1995P $1 Olympics, Gymnastics (PR)	13.00	2009P $1 Lincoln (MS & PR)	15.00
1995D $1 Paralympics (MS)	25.00	2010W $1 Veterans (MS & PR)	15.00
1995S $1 Paralympics (PR)	13.00	2010P $1 100th Anniv. Scouts (MS & PR)	15.00
1995 W or P $1 Special Olympics	13.00	2011 P&S 50¢ U.S. Army (MS & PR)	15.00
1995D $1 Olympics, Track & Field (MS)	25.00	2011 P&S $1 U.S. Army (MS & PR)	15.00
1995P $1 Olympics, Track & Field (PR)	13.00	2012 P&S $1 Infantry Soldier (MS & PR)	15.00
1996S 50¢ Olympics, Soccer (MS)	50.00	2012 P&S $1 Star-Spangled Banner (MS&PR)	15.00
1996S 50¢ Olympics, Soccer (PR)	25.00	2013 P&S $1 Girl Scouts	15.00
1996S 50¢ Olympics, Swimming (MS)	50.00	2013 P&S 50c 5-Star Generals	8.00
1996S 50¢ Olympics, Swimming (PR)	15.00	2013 P&S $1 5-Star Generals (MS & PR)	15.00

Note: (MS) Mint State
(PR) Proof. Coin has mirror finish.

WORLD GOLD COINS

This partial listing of common world gold coins indicates the prices dealers are willing to pay based on the Canadian dollar gold price, September 7th, 2015, of $1,488.00 Canadian funds per ounce. Prices will fluctuate with the price of gold.

AUSTRIA

Date and Denom.	Fine Gold Content Oz.	Buying Price
1912 10K	0.0980	131.00
1915 20K	0.1960	262.00
1915 100K	0.9803	1,310.00
1915 1D	0.1109	150.00
1914 4D	0.4438	600.00
1892 10Fr	0.0933	130.00
1892 20Fr*	0.1867	260.00

BAHAMAS

Date and Denom.	Fine Gold Content Oz.	Buying Price
1967 $10	0.1177	160.00
1971 $10	0.1177	160.00
1972 $10	0.0940	130.00
1967 $20	0.2355	320.00
1971 $20*	0.2355	320.00
1972 $20	0.1880	260.00
1967 $50	0.5888	820.00
1971 $50	0.5888	820.00
1972 $50	0.4708	640.00
1967 $100	1.1776	1,600.00
1971 $100	1.1776	1,600.00
1972 $100	0.9420	1,280.00

BELGIUM

Date and Denom.	Fine Gold Content Oz.	Buying Price
1867 to 1914 20Fr	0.1867	260.00

BERMUDA

Date and Denom.	Fine Gold Content Oz.	Buying Price
1970 $20	0.2355	320.00
1977 $50	0.1172	160.00
1975 $100*	0.2304	315.00
1977 $100	0.2344	320.00

CAYMAN ISLANDS

Date and Denom.	Fine Gold Content Oz.	Buying Price
1972 $25*	0.2222	310.00
1974 $50	0.1823	250.00
1974 $100	0.3646	500.00
1975 $100	0.3646	500.00
1977 $100	0.3646	500.00

* Coin illustrated

CHILE

Date and Denom.	Fine Gold Content Oz.	Buying Price
1898 to 1900 5p	0.0883	120.00
1896 to 1901 10p*	0.1766	240.00
1896 to 1917 20p	0.3532	480.00
1926 to 1980 100p	0.5886	820.00

COLOMBIA

Date and Denom.	Fine Gold Content Oz.	Buying Price
1913 to 1929 2 ½ p	0.1177	160.00
1913 to 1930 5p	0.2355	320.00
1919 and 1924 10p	0.4710	640.00
1973 1500p*	0.5527	765.00

FRANCE

Date and Denom.	Fine Gold Content Oz.	Buying Price
1856 to 1869 5Fr	0.0467	65.00
1854 to 1914 10Fr	0.0933	130.00
1809 to 1914 20Fr*	0.1867	260.00
1810 to 1838 40Fr	0.3734	520.00
1855 to 1864 50Fr	0.4667	645.00
1855 to 1913 100Fr	0.9335	1,290.00

* Coin illustrated

GERMANY

Date and Denom.	Fine Gold Content Oz.	Buying Price
1872 to 1914 10DM	0.1152	155.00
1871 to 1914 20DM*	0.2304	310.00

GREAT BRITAIN

Date and Denom.	Fine Gold Content Oz.	Buying Price
1863 to 1915 ½ Sov.	0.1177	160.00
1871 to 1968 Sov.*	0.2354	320.00
1887 Two Pound	0.4708	640.00
1897 Two Pound	0.4708	640.00
1902 Two Pound	0.4708	640.00
1911 Two Pound	0.4708	640.00
1937 Two Pound	0.4708	640.00
1887 Five Pound	1.1773	1,600.00
1897 Five Pound	1.1773	1,600.00
1902 Five Pound	1.1773	1,600.00
1911 Five Pound	1.1773	1,600.00
1937 Five Pound	1.1773	1,600.00

IRAN

Date and Denom.	Fine Gold Content Oz.	Buying Price
1971 500R	0.1883	260.00
1971 750R*	0.2827	390.00
1971 1000R	0.3770	520.00
1971 2000R	0.7541	1,040.00

ITALY

Date and Denom.	Fine Gold Content Oz.	Buying Price
1932 to 1860 10L	0.0931	130.00
1831 to 1860 20L*	0.1867	260.00
1822 to 1831 40L	0.3733	520.00
1832 to 1844 100L	0.9332	1,300.00

NETHERLANDS

Date and Denom.	Fine Gold Content Oz.	Buying Price
1900 to 1937 1D*	0.1109	150.00
1912 5G	0.0973	135.00
1875 to 1933 10G	0.1947	270.00

JAMAICA

Date and Denom.	Fine Gold Content Oz.	Buying Price
1972 $20*	0.2531	350.00
1975, 1976 $100	0.2265	315.00
1978 $100	0.3281	455.00
1978, 1979 $250	1.2507	1,735.00

PANAMA

Date and Denom.	Fine Gold Content Oz.	Buying Price
1975 to 1979 100B*	0.2361	320.00
1975 to 1979 500B	1.2067	1,60000

MEXICO

Date and Denom.	Fine Gold Content Oz.	Buying Price
1945 2p	0.0482	65.00
1945 2 1/2p	0.0602	80.00
1955 5p	0.1205	165.00
1959 10p*	0.2411	330.00
1959 20p	0.4823	660.00
1947 50p	1.2057	1,650.00

Above dates are restrikes.

RUSSIA

Date and Denom.	Fine Gold Content Oz.	Buying Price
1897 to 1911 5R*	0.1244	170.00
1897 7 1/2R	0.1867	255.00
1898 to 1911 10R	0.2489	340.00
1897 15R	0.3734	510.00
1977 to 1988 100R	0.5000	690.00

*Coin Illustrated

IMPORTANT: Buying prices listed are for coins graded VF or better. Bent, damaged or badly worn coins may be worth less.

BULLION VALUES

Silver and gold coins and other numismatic items are often bought by dealers for their bullion value, that is the value of the pure precious metals which they contain. The weight of precious metals is expressed in grams or troy ounces, not in avoirdupois ounces. A troy ounce is greater than an avoirdupois ounce.

1 Troy Ounce = 31.1035 Grams
1 Avoirdupois Ounce = 28.349 Grams

GOLD

The quantity of pure gold in gold coins is calculated by multiplying the gold fineness or purity of the coin by its weight in troy ounces or grams. Gold purity can also be expressed in karats, a 24-part system with 24-karats equalling pure gold, 22 karats equalling 22 parts gold to 2 parts base metal, 18 karats equalling 18 parts gold to 6 parts base metal etc.

Karats	Fineness	Purity
24	.999	99.9%
22	.916	91.6%
18	.750	75.0%
14	.585	58.5%
10	.417	41.7%
9	.375	37.5%

One 14-karat or .585 fine gold coin weighing 1 troy ounce contains 1 ounce x .585 = .585 troy ounces of pure gold. If gold is worth $1,500 per troy ounce, then this coin is worth $1,500 x .585 = $877.50. (See extended charts on following pages.)

SILVER

The quantity of pure silver in silver coins is calculated by multiplying the silver fineness or purity of the coin by its weight in troy ounces.

Description	Fineness	Purity
Pure	.9999	99.99%
Fine	.999	99.9%
Sterling	.925	92.5%
Coin	.800	80.0%
Coin	.500	50.0%

A .800 fine silver coin weighing 1 troy ounce contains 1 x .800 = .800 troy ounces of pure silver. If silver is worth $30 an ounce, then this coin is worth $30 x .800 = $24. (See extended charts on following pages.)

GOLD CONTENT OF CANADIAN GOLD COINS

Denom.	Date and Mint Mark	Gross Weight		Pure Gold Content	
		Grams	Fineness	Grams	Troy Oz.
1 cent	2012	1.27	.9999	1.27	.040
25 cents	2010-2011, 2013	0.50	.9999	0.50	.016
50 cents	2011-2013	1.27	.9999	1.27	.040
$1	2006-2008	1.555	.9999	1.55	.050
1 Sov.	1908C-1910C	7.99	.917	7.32	.236
1 Sov.	1911C-1919C	7.99	.917	7.32	.236
$2 Nfld.	1865-1888	3.33	.917	3.05	.100
$5	1912-1914	8.36	.900	7.52	.242
$5	2002	8.36	.900	7.52	.242
$5	2011-2013	3.13	.9999	3.13	.100
$10	1912-1914	16.72	.900	15.05	.484
$10	2002	16.72	.900	15.05	.484
$20	1967	18.27	.900	16.45	.529
$5 M.L.	1982 to date	3.11	.9999	3.11	.100
$10 M.L.	1982 to date	7.78	.9999	7.78	.250
$20 M.L.	1986 to date	15.57	.9999	15.57	.500
$25	2013	7.797	.9999	7.797	.250
$50 M.L.	1979 to date	31.10	.999	31.10	1.000
$50	2005	12.00	.5833	7.00	.225
$50	2012	33.17	.99999	33.17	1.066
$75	2005	31.44	.4166	13.10	.421
$75	2007-2010	12.00	.5833	7.00	.225
$75	2013	7.80	.9999	7.80	.250
$100	1976 (Unc.)	13.33	.583	7.78	.250
$100	1976 (Proof)	16.96	.917	15.55	.500
$100	1977-1986	16.96	.917	15.55	.500
$100	1987-2003	13.33	.583	7.78	.250
$100	2004 to date	12.00	.583	7.00	.225
$150	2000-2003	13.61	.75	10.20	.328
$150	2004-2011	11.84	.750	8.88	.285
$150	2009-2012	10.40	.99999	10.40	.334
$150	2010-2013	11.70	.75	8.78	.282
$150	2013	15.59	.9999	15.59	.500
$175	1992	16.97	.916	15.556	.500
$200	1990-2003	17.106	.916	15.669	.500
$200	2004-2011	16.00	.917	14.67	.471
$200	2012-2013	15.43	.9999	15.43	.500
$200	2012	31.10	.9999	31.10	1.00
$200	2013	33.33	.9999	33.33	1.07
$250	2006	45.00	.5833	26.235	.843
$300 (50mm)	2002-2013	60.00	.5833	35.00	1.125
$300 (40mm)	2005-2008	45.00	.5833	26.25	.844
$300 (25mm)	2012	22.00	.99999	22.00	.707
$350 Thick	1998-2003	38.05	.99999	38.05	1.222
$350 Thin	2004-2011	35.00	.99999	35.00	1.125
$350	2012	35.00	.99999	35.00	1.125
$500	2007-2012	155.76	.9999	155.76	5.010
$2,500	2007-2013	1000.00	.9999	1000.00	32.150

DOLLAR VALUES OF CANADIAN GOLD COINS

Computed from $1,250. to $2,250. per troy ounce in increments of $250 Canadian.

Denom.	Date and Mint Mark	$1,250.	$1,500.	$1,750.	$2,000.	$2,250.
1 cent	2012	50.	60.	70.	80.	90.
25 cents	2010	20.	24.	28.	32.	36.
50 cents	2011-2013	50.	60.	70.	80.	90.
$1	2006-2008	62.	75.	87.	100.	112.
1 Sov.	1908C-1910C	295.	354.	413.	472.	531.
1 Sov.	1911C-1919C	295.	354.	413.	472.	531.
$2 Nfld.	1865-1888	125.	150.	175.	200.	225.
$5	1912-1914	302.	363.	423.	484.	544.
$5	2002	302.	363.	423.	484.	544.
$5	2011-2013	125.	150.	175.	200.	225.
$10	1912-1914	605.	726.	847.	968.	1,089.
$10	2002	605.	726.	847.	968.	1,089.
$20	1967	660.	794.	926.	1,058.	1,190.
$5 M.L.	1982 to date	125.	150.	175.	200.	225.
$10 M.L.	1982 to date	312.	375.	438.	500.	563.
$20 M.L.	1986 to date	625.	750.	875.	1,000.	1,125.
$25	2013	312.	375.	438.	500.	563.
$50 M.L.	1979 to date	1,250.	1,500.	1,750.	2,000.	2,250.
$50	2005	280.	337.	394.	450.	506.
$50	2012	1,332.	1600.	1,865.	2,132.	2,398.
$75	2005	526.	631.	737.	842.	947.
$75	2007-2010	280.	337.	394.	450.	506.
$75	2013	312.	375.	438.	500.	563.
$100	1976 (Unc)	312.	375.	438.	500.	563.
$100	1976 (Proof)	625.	750.	875.	1,000.	1,125.
$100	1977-1986	625.	750.	875.	1,000.	1,125.
$100	1987-2003	312.	375.	438.	500.	563.
$100	2004 to date	280.	338.	394.	450.	506.
$150	2000-2003	410.	492.	574.	656.	738.
$150	2004-2011	356.	428.	499.	570.	641.
$150	2009-2012	417.	501.	584.	668.	751.
$150	2010-2013	352.	423.	493.	564.	634.
$150	2013	625.	750.	875.	1,000.	1,125.
$175	1992	625.	750.	875.	1,000.	1,125.
$200	1990-2003	625.	750.	875.	1,000.	1,125.
$200	2004-2011	589.	706.	824.	942.	1,060.
$200	2012-2013	625.	750.	875.	1,000.	1,125.
$200	2012	1,250.	1,500.	1,750.	2,000.	2,250.
$200	2013	1,337.	1,605.	1,872.	2,140.	2,407.
$250	2006	1,054.	1,265.	1,475.	1,686.	1,897.
$300	2002 to 2013 (50mm)	1,406.	1,687.	1,969.	2,250.	2,531.
$300	2005 to 2008 (40mm)	1,054.	1,265.	1,475.	1,686.	1,897.
$300	2012 (25mm)	884.	1,060.	1,237.	1,414.	1,591.
$350	1998-2003 (thick)	1,527.	1,833.	2,138.	2,444.	2,750.
$350	2004-2011 (thin)	1,406.	1,688.	1,969.	2,250.	2,531.
$350	2012	1,406.	1,688.	1,969.	2,250.	2,531.
$500	2007-2010	6,262.	7,515.	8,767.	10,020.	11,272.
$2,500	2007-2013	40,187.	48,225.	56,262.	64,300.	72,337.

SILVER CONTENT OF CANADIAN SILVER COINS

Denom.	Date	Gross Weight		Silver Content	
		Grams	Fineness	Grams	Troy Oz.
3 cents	2001	5.35	.925	4.95	.159
5 cents	1858-1919, 1998	1.16	.925	1.08	.035
5 cents	1920-1921	1.16	.800	.933	.030
5 cents	2000-2005	5.30	.925	4.90	.158
10 cents	1858-1919	2.33	.925	2.146	.069
10 cents	1920-1967	2.33	.800	1.866	.060
10 cents	1967-1968	2.33	.500	1.170	.038
10 cents	1997-2004	2.40	.925	2.22	.071
25 cents	1870-1919	5.81	.925	5.370	.173
25 cents	1920-1967	5.83	.800	4.665	.150
25 cents	1967-1968	5.83	.500	2.923	.094
25 cents	1992-2009	5.90	.925	5.458	.175
25 cents	1998 (90th)	5.81	.925	5.374	.173
50 cents	1870-1919	11.66	.925	10.792	.347
50 cents	1920-1967	11.66	.800	9.330	.300
50 cents	1995-2005	9.30	.925	8.603	.277
50 cents	2008 (triangular)	20.00	.925	18.50	.595
$1	1935-1967	23.30	.800	18.661	.600
$1	1971-1991	23.30	.500	11.65	.375
$1	1992-2002	25.18	.925	23.29	.750
$1	2003-2006	25.18	.9999	25.17	.809
$1	2007-2010	25.18	.925	23.29	.750
$1 Loon	2004-2010	7.00	.925	6.475	.208
$2	2004	8.8	.925	8.14	.262
$3	2006 (square)	11.72	.925	10.84	.349
$3	2010	7.96	.9999	7.96	.256
$3	2010 (square)	12.00	.925	11.1	.357
$4	2007-2010	15.87	.9999	15.87	.510
$5	1973-1976	24.30	.925	22.48	.720
$5 M.L.	1988 to date	31.04	.9999	31.1035	1.000
$5	2001	16.96	.925	15.69	.504
$5	2003	31.30	.9999	31.30	1.010
$5	2004-2006	28.00	.9999	28.00	.900
$5	2005, 2006, 2009	25.175	.9999	25.17	.810
$8	2004	28.80	.925	26.64	.856
$8	2005	32.15	.9999	32.15	1.030
$8	2007	25.18	.9999	25.18	.810
$8	2009-2010	25.30	.925	23.40	.752
$10	1973-1976	48.60	.925	44.95	1.44
$10	2005-2006	25.175	.9999	25.175	.810
$10	2010	27.78	.925	25.70	.826
$10	2010	15.90	.9999	15.90	.511
$15	1992, 1998-2009	33.63	.925	31.108	1.000
$15	2008-2009	30.00	.925	27.75	.890
$15	2008-2009 (oblong)	31.56	.925	29.193	.938
$15	2010-2011 (scalloped)	26.30	.925	24.327	.782
$15	2010-2011	31.39	.9999	31.39	1.01
$20	1985-1987	34.07	.925	31.51	1.01
$20	1990-2003	31.10	.925	28.77	.925
$20	2003-2010	31.39	.9999	31.39	1.01
$20	2007	27.78	.925	25.70	.826
$20	2007	50.10	.925	46.34	1.49
$20	2008-2009	27.78	.925	25.70	.826
$25	2007-2009	27.78	.925	25.70	.826
$30	2005-2008	31.50	.925	29.137	.937
$50	2006-2013	156.36	.9999	156.34	5.026
$250	2007-2013	1000.00	.9999	1000.00	32.151

DOLLAR VALUES OF CANADIAN SILVER COINS

Computed from $20 to $70 per troy ounce in increments of $10 Canadian.

Denom.	Date	$20	$30	$40	$50	$60	$70
3-cents	2001	3.18	4.77	6.36	7.95	9.54	11.13
5 cents	1858-1919, 1998	.70	1.05	1.40	1.75	2.10	2.45
5 cents	1920-1921	.60	.90	1.20	1.50	1.80	2.10
5 cents	2000-2005	3.16	4.74	6.32	7.90	9.48	11.06
10 cents	1858-1919	1.38	2.07	2.76	3.45	4.14	4.83
10 cents	1920-1967	1.20	1.80	2.40	3.00	3.60	4.20
10 cents	1967-1968	.76	1.14	1.52	1.90	2.28	2.66
10 cents	1997-2004	1.42	2.13	2.84	3.55	4.26	4.97
25 cents	1870-1919	3.46	5.19	6.92	8.65	10.38	12.11
25 cents	1920-1967	3.00	4.50	6.00	7.50	9.00	10.50
25 cents	1967-1968	1.88	2.82	3.76	4.70	5.64	6.58
25 cents	1992-2009	3.50	5.25	7.00	8.75	10.50	12.25
25 cents	1998 (90th)	3.46	5.19	6.92	8.65	10.38	12.11
50 cents	1870-1919	6.94	10.41	13.88	17.35	20.82	24.29
50 cents	1920-1967	6.00	9.00	12.00	15.00	18.00	21.00
50 cents	1995-2005	5.54	8.31	11.08	13.85	16.62	19.39
50 cents	2008 (triangular)	11.90	17.85	23.80	29.75	35.70	41.65
$1	1935-1967	12.00	18.00	24.00	30.00	36.00	42.00
$1	1971-1991	7.50	11.25	15.00	18.75	22.50	26.25
$1	1992-2002	15.00	22.50	30.00	37.50	45.00	52.50
$1	2003-2006	16.18	24.27	32.36	40.45	48.54	56.63
$1	2007-2010	15.00	22.50	30.00	37.50	45.00	52.50
$1 Loon	2004-2010	4.16	6.24	8.32	10.40	12.48	14.56
$2	2004	5.24	7.86	10.48	13.10	15.72	18.34
$3	2006 (square)	6.98	10.47	13.96	17.45	20.94	24.43
$3	2010	5.12	7.68	10.50	12.80	15.36	17.92
$4	2007-2010	10.20	15.30	20.40	25.50	30.60	35.70
$5	1973-1976	14.40	21.60	28.80	36.00	43.20	50.40
$5 M.L.	1988 to date	20.00	30.00	40.00	50.00	60.00	70.00
$5	2001	10.08	15.12	20.16	25.20	30.24	35.28
$5	2003	20.20	30.30	40.40	50.50	60.60	70.70
$5	2004-2006	18.00	27.00	36.00	45.00	54.00	63.00
$5	2005, 2006, 2009	16.20	24.30	32.40	40.50	48.60	56.70
$8	2004	17.12	25.68	34.24	42.80	51.36	59.92
$8	2005	20.60	30.90	41.20	51.50	61.80	72.10
$8	2007	16.20	24.30	32.40	40.50	48.60	56.70
$8	2009-2010	15.04	22.56	30.66	38.76	46.86	54.96
$10	1973-1976	28.80	43.35	57.80	72.25	86.70	101.15
$10	2005-2006	16.20	24.30	32.40	40.50	48.60	56.70
$10	2010	16.52	24.78	33.04	41.30	49.56	57.82
$10	2010	10.22	15.33	20.44	25.55	30.66	35.77
$15	1992, 1998-2009	20.00	30.00	40.00	50.00	60.00	70.00
$15	2008-2009	17.80	26.70	35.60	44.50	53.40	62.30
$15	2008-2013 (oblong)	18.76	28.14	37.52	46.90	56.28	65.66
$15	2010-2013 (scalloped)	15.64	23.46	31.28	39.10	46.92	54.74
$15	2010-2011	20.20	30.30	40.40	50.50	60.60	70.70
$20	1985-1987	20.20	30.30	40.40	50.50	60.60	70.70
$20	1990-2003	18.50	27.75	37.00	46.25	55.50	64.75
$20	2003-2010	20.20	30.30	40.40	50.50	60.60	70.70
$20	2007-2009	16.52	24.78	33.04	41.30	49.56	57.82
$20	2007	29.80	44.70	59.60	74.50	89.40	104.30
$25	2007-2009	16.52	24.78	33.04	41.30	49.56	57.82
$30	2005-2008	18.74	28.11	37.48	46.85	56.22	65.59
$50	2006-2013	100.52	150.78	201.04	251.30	301.56	351.82
$250	2007-2013	643.02	964.53	1,286.04	1,607.55	1,929.06	2,250.57

PALLADIUM CONTENT OF CANADIAN PALLADIUM COINS

Denom.	Date	Gross Weight		Platinum Content	
		Grams	Fineness	Grams	Troy Oz.
$50	2006	31.16	.9995	31.16	1.000

DOLLAR VALUES OF CANADIAN PALLADIUM COINS

Denom.	Date and Mint Mark	$800.	$900.	$1,000.	$1,100.	$1,200.
$50	2006	800.	900.	1,000.	1,100.	1,200.

PLATINUM CONTENT OF CANADIAN PLATINUM COINS

Denom.	Date	Gross Weight		Platinum Content	
		Grams	Fineness	Grams	Troy Oz.
$30	1990-2004	3.12	.9995	3.12	.100
$75	1990-2004	7.79	.9995	7.79	.250
$150	1990-2004	15.58	.9995	15.58	.500
$300	1990-2004	31.13	.9995	31.16	1.000
Set: 4 Coins		57.65	.9995	57.65	1.85
$300	2007-2010	31.16	.9995	31.14	1.00

DOLLAR VALUES OF CANADIAN PLATINUM COINS

Denom.	Date and Mint Mark	$1,500.	$1,750.	$2,000.	$2,250.	$2,500.
$30	1990-2004	150.	175.	200.	225.	250.
$75	1990-2004	375.	438.	500.	563.	625.
$150	1990-2004	750.	875.	1,000.	1,125.	1,250.
$300	1990-2010	1,500.	1,750.	2,000.	2,250.	2,500.
Set: 4 coins	1990-2004	2,775.	3,238.	3,700.	4,163.	4,625.
$300	2007-2010	1,500.	1,750.	2,000.	2.250.	2,500.